D0378703

Symposium on
BASIC RESEARCH

Symposium on
BASIC
RESEARCH

Sponsored by
THE NATIONAL ACADEMY OF SCIENCES,
THE AMERICAN ASSOCIATION FOR THE
ADVANCEMENT OF SCIENCE, AND
THE ALFRED P. SLOAN FOUNDATION,
and presented at the Caspary Auditorium of the
Rockefeller Institute,
May 14-16, 1959, New York City

DAEL WOLFLE, Editor

Publication No. 56 of the
AMERICAN ASSOCIATION FOR THE ADVANCEMENT OF SCIENCE
WASHINGTON, D. C.   1959

Copyright © 1959 by

The American Association for the Advancement of Science

LIBRARY OF CONGRESS CATALOG CARD NUMBER 59-15334

PRINTED IN THE UNITED STATES

507.2
S 9895

141233

PROGRAM

SESSION I *Thursday, May 14*

Official Welcome
> Dr. Detlev W. Bronk, *President, The Rockefeller Institute*

Chairman, Dr. George W. Beadle, *California Institute of Technology*

PAPERS PRESENTED

> THE IMPORTANCE OF NEW KNOWLEDGE
> Dr. J. Robert Oppenheimer
> > *Institute for Advanced Study*

> BASIC RESEARCH IN THE UNITED STATES
> Dr. Alan T. Waterman
> > *National Science Foundation*

> THE PARADOX OF CHOICE
> Dr. William O. Baker
> > *Bell Telephone Laboratories*

PANEL DISCUSSION

> Discussion Leader, Dr. George W. Beadle

Panel (in addition to the speakers)

> Dr. Lawrence R. Hafstad, *General Motors Corporation*
> Dr. Joseph C. Hinsey, *New York Hospital-Cornell Medical Center*
> Dr. Ernst Mayr, *Harvard University*

.v

Mills College Library
MILLS COLLEGE
Withdrawn
LIBRARY

Dr. Harry L. Shapiro, *American Museum of Natural History*

Rapporteur, Dr. Gerald Holton, *Harvard University*

SESSION II *Thursday, May 14*

Chairman, Dr. John S. Dickey, *Dartmouth College*

PAPERS PRESENTED

BASIC RESEARCH AND THE LIBERAL ARTS COLLEGE
Dr. Laurence M. Gould
Carleton College

BASIC RESEARCH AND THE STATE UNIVERSITY
Dr. Conrad A. Elvehjem
University of Wisconsin

BASIC RESEARCH AND THE PRIVATE UNIVERSITY
Dr. Lee A. DuBridge
California Institute of Technology

PANEL DISCUSSION

Discussion Leader, Dr. John S. Dickey

Panel (in addition to the speakers)

Dr. David R. Goddard, *University of Pennsylvania*
Dr. William V. Houston, *The Rice Institute*
Dr. Deane Montgomery, *Institute for Advanced Study*
Dr. William E. Stevenson, *Oberlin College*

Rapporteur, Dean Mary I. Bunting, *Douglass College*

SESSION III *Thursday, May 14*

Presiding, Dr. Detlev W. Bronk, *President, The Rockefeller Institute*

PAPERS PRESENTED

Dr. James R. Killian, Jr.
Special Assistant to the President for Science and Technology

Mr. Crawford H. Greenewalt
*President, E. I. du Pont de Nemours &
Company*

Dwight D. Eisenhower
President of the United States

SESSION IV *Friday, May 15*

Chairman, Dr. James A. Shannon, *National Institutes of
Health*

PAPERS PRESENTED

BASIC RESEARCH IN GOVERNMENT LABORATORIES
Dr. Allen V. Astin
National Bureau of Standards

BASIC RESEARCH IN INDUSTRIAL LABORATORIES
Dr. James B. Fisk
Bell Telephone Laboratories

BASIC RESEARCH IN PRIVATE RESEARCH INSTITUTES
Dr. Merle A. Tuve
Carnegie Institution of Washington

PANEL DISCUSSION

Discussion Leader, Dr. James A. Shannon

Panel (in addition to the speakers)

Dr. Paul J. Flory, *Mellon Institute*
Dr. Isidor I. Rabi, *Columbia University*
Dr. C. Guy Suits, *General Electric Company*
Dr. Max Tishler, *Merck Sharp & Dohme*

Rapporteur, Dr. Douglas Whitaker, *The Rockefeller
Institute*

SESSION V *Friday, May 15*

Chairman, Dr. Lloyd V. Berkner, *Associated Universities,
Inc.*

PAPERS PRESENTED

SUPPORT OF BASIC RESEARCH FROM GOVERNMENT
Dr. Paul E. Klopsteg
National Science Foundation

SUPPORT OF BASIC RESEARCH FROM INDUSTRY
Dr. Robert E. Wilson
*Former Chairman of the Board, Standard Oil
Company (Indiana)*

SUPPORT OF BASIC RESEARCH FROM PRIVATE
PHILANTHROPY
Dr. Robert S. Morison
The Rockefeller Foundation

PANEL DISCUSSION

Discussion Leader, Dr. Lloyd V. Berkner

Panel (in addition to the speakers)

Dr. Hugh L. Dryden, *National Aeronautics and
Space Administration*
Dr. Julian W. Hill, *E. I. du Pont de Nemours &
Company*
Mr. J. William Hinkley, *Research Corporation*
Dean Don K. Price, *Harvard University*

Rapporteur, Dr. Harry C. Kelly, *National Science
Foundation*

DISCUSSION SESSION   *Saturday, May 16*

The persons on the list of participants (page 281) whose
names are marked by an asterisk participated in this discussion session.

Chairman and Discussion Leader, Dr. Julius A. Stratton,
Massachusetts Institute of Technology

RAPPORTEURS

Dr. Graham DuShane, *American Association for the Advancement of Science*

Dr. Walter A. Rosenblith, *Massachusetts Institute of Technology*

Symposium Editor, Dr. Dael Wolfle, *American Association for the Advancement of Science*

PREFACE

Science is important: there can be no doubt that the modern world recognizes this fact. Even those who deprecate its possible consequences are reluctant to be without its resources.

Science deserves support: everyone agrees to this also, especially if each is permitted to give his own definition of science and how it is to be supported.

But what is important about science; what science really is; what scientific activities are "practical" and what visionary and presumably lacking in significance; what kind and amount of support society ought to furnish to scientists; what balance there should be between the support of *basic science*—the untrammeled search for new knowledge for its own sake—and of *applied science*—the search for and the use of knowledge specifically needed for recognized practical objectives; these are puzzling and unanswered questions.

Some five years ago General Lucius Clay, a Trustee of the Alfred P. Sloan Foundation, suggested to that philanthropic organization that the physical sciences, particularly the basic fields of chemistry, mathematics, and physics, could profitably use more financial assistance based not upon specific "project" proposals, but based upon the demonstrated capacity of the recipient scientists, young persons of intelligence and character, to carry out creative and significant research in general fields of their own choosing.

The resulting program, which is directed by Dr. Richard T. Arnold, has now reached a level of approximately one million dollars a year. Some 118 individuals, of median age of about 32, receive annual sums ranging from $6,000 to $14,000 or even higher, the amount of the grant depending on the particular individual's need for unencumbered research funds. There is practically complete freedom as to the detailed way in which the money is to be used; and the recipients make no commitments whatsoever as to what particular problems they will consider. There is no possible necessity of making any rash promise of problems which will be "solved." There is no temptation to establish some putative relation with a popular topic. There is no embarrassment whatsoever about reorientation of activity if and when interesting and unexpected new leads develop.

The recipients of these grants do not apply for them. Rather they are sought out by the Sloan Foundation officer, who has the invaluable advice of a small but nation-wide group of consultants, picked specially for their knowledge of and interest in young scientists.

The experience to date with this program has been so promising that the Sloan Foundation became convinced that science would profit if a greater number of dedicated scientists could have support of this broad and flexible character. Consideration of this need led, in turn, to the idea of holding a discussion of the support of basic research, with nation-wide participation of academic, industrial, and government scientists; of administrators responsible for research activities in universities, colleges, private research institutes, government, and industry; and of individuals who are at the decision level with respect to general policies concerning scientific research.

It became clear at once to the Sloan Foundation group discussing such a meeting that it was most desirable that any such meeting have the broadest and most authoritative sponsorship. The National Academy of Sciences, as the nation's top-ranking scientific organization, and the American Association for the Advancement of Science, as the nation's one large and widely representative scientific organization, were approached; and both enthusiastically agreed to join the Sloan Foundation in the sponsorship of the meeting. The financial support was furnished by the Sloan Foundation.

The planning of the Symposium thus proceeded under the general chairmanship of Dr. Detlev W. Bronk, President of the National Academy of Sciences; Dr. Paul E. Klopsteg, President of the American Association for the Advancement of Science; and Mr. Alfred P. Sloan, Jr., President of the Sloan Foundation. The Arrangements Committee consisted of Dr. S. D. Cornell from the National Academy staff, Dr. Dael Wolfle from the AAAS, Dr. Richard T. Arnold of the Sloan Foundation, and Dr. Warren Weaver of The Rockefeller Foundation* as Chairman of the Arrangements Committee and Program Coordinator.

The meetings were held at The Rockefeller Institute in New York City, where the participants had the privilege of utilizing the extraordinarily attractive and effective facilities of the Caspary Auditorium, the various dining and lounging rooms, ample space for service staff, a news room, etc.

In inviting the participants, the following statement was included:

Experience during and since World War II has emphasized the importance that science, viewed as a whole, be energetically developed in our country. As a response, there has occurred a vast expansion of our total activity in research and development.

Much of the technical advance during and directly after the war was based, as is now generally recognized, on fundamental scientific knowledge that had been produced not in our own country or by in-

* Dr. Weaver retired as Vice President for the Natural and Medical Sciences in The Rockefeller Foundation on July 31, 1959, and on August 1 became Vice President of the Alfred P. Sloan Foundation.

dividuals educated here, but rather by scholars in and of other countries. Indeed, after the war it was often said that while we are clever and energetic about exploiting ideas, we have not seemed equally effective in the discovery of new knowledge and in the production of imaginative new ideas.

Strong evidence has been accumulating that we are in fact capable of creating new knowledge. But in spite of our verbal dedication to the importance of basic research, and in spite of our emerging confidence that we have the national resources of imaginative, competent, and dedicated individuals to carry out basic research, it nevertheless remains true that *as a nation, we are not giving adequate and suitable support to basic research.* Consider the following questions:

1. Is not the large support of applied research, and still more particularly the massive present support of development, in unhealthy relation to the meager support for basic research?
2. Is it not true that industry pays eager lip service to basic research, but in actual fact does not give adequate support to basic research, either within industry or elsewhere?
3. Has either industry or government learned how to protect basic research from the insistent demands of applied research and development?
4. Are not universities so deeply invaded by the demands for solving immediate problems and by the temptation of income for so doing, that there are all too few cases of competent scholars pondering about problems simply because it interests them to do so? Is there not a real danger that the scholars in our universities will lose—and indeed have already partly lost—the "maneuvering room for their continuing reanalysis of the universe?"
5. Has it been effectively accepted in our country that the spirit of basic research is an essential ingredient of the educational process—and that this fact should affect educational procedures at all levels?

The difficulty is not a simple one of fiscal arithmetic. More funds for basic research are indeed required: but of even greater importance is the way in which basic research funds are made available—the flexibility, the stability, the freedom from intellectually dishonest commitment, with which competent scholarship should be supported.

It is the purpose of this Symposium to set forth and examine with candor the facts concerning the support of basic research in our country; to inquire realistically what are the blocks which prevent our doing what we all say we believe is important; to make concrete suggestions as to ways in which the situation can be improved; and in general to proclaim the fundamental faith which we have in the importance of free and imaginative basic research, and to do this with such competence and vigor as will have a national impact.

Those associated with the actual conduct of the Symposium owe a great debt to Dr. Bronk and to The Rockefeller Institute for most generous and lovely hospitality, to the staffs of The Rockefeller Institute, the National Academy of Sciences, the AAAS, and the Sloan Foundation for their many hours of efficient and extra work. Mr. Willcox B. Adsit of the General Motors Acceptance Corporation was invaluable in assisting with all the complicated arrangements for the banquet at the Waldorf. The firm of Ivy Lee and T. J. Ross handled all press and public relations aspects with taste and efficiency, Mr. J. M. Ripley and Mr. William A. Paddock being primarily responsible. Miss Ruth Abramson and Miss Helena Curtis, of the public relations staff of the Memorial Center, gave important assistance in connection with press releases of the technical papers. Miss Virginia Tolson, on a temporary assignment at the Sloan Foundation for this special purpose, was of great help in handling many aspects of the detailed arrangements. Very special thanks are due to the press, radio, television, and magazine representatives for their interested presence and for their effective handling of the news. The tally is not complete even yet, but over 800 press clippings, editorials, etc., from all over the nation, have been noted thus far.

The success of the Symposium depended in an obvious and essential way on the services and abilities of the speakers, the chairmen, and the rapporteurs. A very special thanks is clearly due to this group.

The writer is not really clear about the etiquette of thanking the President of the United States. But certainly the presence of Mr. Eisenhower at the Symposium banquet and the wise and understanding things he said in his speech gave the scientific fraternity of this country a feeling of great lift and encouragement and a deep satisfaction that our President would in this way emphasize the importance of the most scholarly aspects of science.

The Committee had planned on an attendance of 250 for the sessions on the first two days. Against the firm advice of certain friends whose principal experience had been with other types of conventions, we set the opening session to start at 9:15 A.M. sharp. On Thursday morning at precisely 9:15 there were a few more than 250 persons in the seats. Having planned on 100 for the final closed session of discussion, the actual number in the seats, not counting the chairman, was 99. Certainly the participants all responded nobly.

It may be useful to make a final comment about the scope of this Symposium. At one juncture in discussing the essential aims of basic research, the writer referred to basic research as "the never-ending search for better understanding of man himself and of the total world, animate and inanimate, in which he lives." As a result, several stirring communications have been received which in effect say, "Man's understanding of himself! Why did the Symposium not include a proper emphasis on the social—or more particularly, the behavioral—sciences? You speak of basic research and seem to assume that this phrase is restricted to the quantitative and analytical natural sciences! Why do you not include, in addition to the social sciences, the humanities, the fine arts, and the philosophical and moral nature of man?"

With respect to the behavioral, or even more generally the social, sciences it can, I think, be soundly argued that the Sym-

xvi

posium did actually not neglect them. It is true that there was no discussion of their content or special problems, but neither was there discussion of the content or special problems of mathematics, or geophysics, or astronomy. The intent was to focus attention on problems general to all scientific work.

With respect to the humanities, fine arts, and indeed the whole range of man's intellectual life, the interesting and significant thing is that, whatever the intended range of topic in the Symposium program, those who attended again and again stressed the fact that the health of any one restricted aspect of science depends upon the health of man's total intellectual effort and program.

As the reader will learn from the summary chapter, the scientists refused to limit their interest to any one compartment of man's creative life and insisted on emphasizing that any proper program of basic research in science be an integral part of a much broader program of support for creative scholarship in the broadest sense of that term.

WARREN WEAVER

August 1959

CONTENTS

CONTENTS

xx

THE NEED FOR NEW KNOWLEDGE

J. ROBERT OPPENHEIMER
The Institute for Advanced Study

> We need new knowledge like we
> need a hole in the head
> 20th Century American Proverb

THE NEED for new knowledge has not always been fully recognized by the authorities, as the story of Adam and the legend of Prometheus remind us. New knowledge has been feared as the destroyer of man's innocence and his virtue, as an incitement to pride and insubordination, and as subversive of public order and social good. It is, of course, guilty of all these charges.

Discovery has been most resisted when it has most deeply altered the terms in which man formulates and understands his place and destiny. Even the description of his physical habitat in space and time was not upset without struggle, without terror, without martyrdom. From its earliest beginnings in Paris to the Newtonian synthesis in the seventeenth century, the universe, closed in space, finite in time, and centered upon the earth, changed, in what then seemed, and largely was, an irre-

I

versible step, to a world infinite in both space and time, in which the earth as one part of an immense machine followed the laws of Kepler and of Newton, a modest planet circling the sun.

At many other times new knowledge has given us a different view of ourselves, has changed the words and the ideas in terms of which we think and talk to one another, has altered, as Butterfield likes to say, "our thinking caps." It is barely a century ago that this happened in our understanding of man's relation to other forms of life; many of us can remember the hostility and suspicion with which the theory of evolution was still greeted in the earlier years of this century. In this country, indeed, the appointments to the presidency of some old, great private universities, made at mid-twentieth century, seem to me to attest a lingering but substantial doubt as to our need for new knowledge.

Those of us who have lived through the great discoveries in atomic mechanics which culminated three decades ago in the quantum theory, have long believed that these, too, had powerful and deep lessons for man's understanding of his own situation, not in this case about his habitat, nor his relations to other forms of life, but about the nature, power, and limits of his knowledge. There has been some dispute about the epistemological interpretation of quantum theory, but very little. In part this may be because the experience it describes is remote from common life, and thus abstract. But a deeper reason is not hard to find. Old beliefs do not afford the basis for spirited resistance to the new, when they are no longer held with firmness and in common understanding. It is fifty years since William James wrote:

> The point I now urge you to observe particularly is the part played by the older truths. . . . Their influence is absolutely controlling. Loyalty to them is the first principle—in most cases it

is the only principle; for by far the most usual way of handling phenomena so novel that they would make for a serious rearrangement of our preconception is to ignore them altogether, or to abuse those who bear witness for them.

Why, then, do we seek new knowledge, and ask for the help of others in enabling us to acquire it? To this question there is not one answer; there are two. They are disturbingly unrelated. Each answer, in turn, in this mid-twentieth century, in our time and country, poses a set of problems that man has never faced before. To these I must return.

One answer is that new knowledge is useful; the other answer is that the getting of it is ennobling. Indeed it is ennobling, as anyone who has spent his life, or an honest part of it, in studying nature can attest. Science today, the study of nature and of man as part of nature, is continuous, despite all that makes it unique in scope, brilliance, and virtuosity, with the long tradition of attempting to comprehend our situation in the world and the world in which we live. The revelation of new and unexpected wonders, the gradual emergence of great architectonic traits of order, the harmony of a world free of inconsistency widen us as men and give us a sense of beauty which is both vast and robust. Repeated discovery that what we took for firm truths are conditional ones, limited by the limitation or poverty of our past experience, gives to this enterprise a quality at once modest and vigorous. We do not argue these matters, or even speak much about them; but in them is rooted the commitment to science of those who practice it; by their example, by the lives and works of men of science, we judge its weight and depth.

Clearly these brave words give an odd and incomplete description of the immense activity which is contemporary science, even in its purest sense, as the disinterested study of nature for the sake of knowledge. Some parts of the order of

3

nature speak to the wonder of men: so it is with the cosmos, in any of the historically varying and expanding uses of that word; so it is with the origin of life, or the nature of heredity, or the nature of memory, and the other higher human functions. But we have learned that wonder resides, and paradox and puzzlement and harmony and order, in many ordinary things: in the stuff that matter is made of, in the flow of the ocean's currents, in the migration of birds, in bubble and drop and clod. We have come to respect the most pedestrian curiosity as a likely origin of learning unexpected and lovely things about our world.

Not every work of science, experiment, observation, calculation is in itself a work of beauty. There is research, there are stories, that confirm and elaborate what we have known, and neither enlarge nor deepen it; there are findings which may lie for years, not helpful in any larger picture, until they are encompassed by discoveries from another source. The words that the mathematicians tend to use to describe their work are "trivial" and "deep." These are words in part of logical assessment, yet essentially of esthetic judgment; they are common to all scientists talking of their trade. We do not explain very well what we mean by them, or how to conduct ourselves and our researches so that they may be deep, and not be trivial. In this we are not so unlike painters or actors or musicians. We can hardly explain; but that we do indeed know something is clear from the fact that we can teach, and that we often find in those whom we have taught a surer instinct and a finer taste than in ourselves or our colleagues.

I have heard Rutherford express impatience with a talented physicist, one for whom we all have the highest regard and affection, and who has been signally honored, because Rutherford saw no chance that in his researches he would discover anything really new or startling or beautiful. Rutherford was right. Yet when we look back over the history of science, we see how often profound new discoveries have originated in almost prospectless investigations: in measuring a little more accurately, in making really sure that radium was a product of the bombardment of uranium by neutrons, in uncounted instances of the detailed and painstaking study of things presumed already known.

It is this that gives to the work of science a special and welcome human quality. It is often illustrated by the metaphor that science is a great house, and that those who work in it lay the bricks. For this work is rewarded by the presence of larger wholes, in which all scientists may and do participate and share, and in which the uninspired and unlucky live in the same large structure as the man of genius. What the men of genius have, that many of the rest of us are spared, is the terror that led Columbus to write, on the first and empty page of his log, on the first evening of his first voyage of discovery,

Jesus cum Maria sit nobis in via.

Many of the words that I have used in talking of the nobility of science could be used as well of the writing of poetry or of music. There are quite other words, and a quite different argument. New knowledge is useful. By knowing more of nature and a little, pitifully little, of ourselves, we know how to make things and do things which otherwise we should not have known how to make or do; and by these increased abilities and powers we in general offer to men a far wider range of choices as to what and how they are to do, what and how they are to make. This has, of course, altered the face of the earth. It has altered it even in parts of the world where the search for new knowledge has as yet played no major part in men's lives. It has altered it even for those who care little, and know less, of the new knowledge which has made the change possible. It has

5

produced a world in which the explosion of the new knowledge is reflected in material and practical terms by a rate of change unprecedented in the world's history. I have no doubt that other papers in this symposium will illustrate with vividness and skill many of the instances in which some finding, some discovery that was made by a curious scholar enquiring of nature to find the truth has been the basis of changes in the human situation, in our habits, in our social order, in our converse with one another, comparable to or greater than any brought about by conquests and revolutions.

In a sense, the connection between new knowledge and new power is as old as history, as old as myth. It was understood by Archimedes, as well as by his Tyrant. But in today's world the inventor and the scientist, though sometimes the same man, are more often distinct; yet they are far more dependent one on the other than in the past. The steam engine and the cotton gin rested on no newly acquired knowledge; they might have been invented earlier, and were perhaps more responsive to a new need and a new opportunity than to a new or better understanding of nature. The zipper may well be the twentieth century's contribution to such invention. But increasingly the practical developments of our time rest on things which were not known to our fathers, and often on things which were not known to us when we went to school.

Manifestly not every finding leads straight to invention; but it is hard to think of major discoveries about nature, major advances in science, which have not had large and ramified practical consequences. I should think that as of today, Einstein's general theory of relativity had had few if any practical consequences. This rests on the inaccessibility of very strong gravitational fields, and our poor powers to create them at will. It is therefore related with the widely held view that general relativity, though very likely to be true, is not very firmly estab-

6

lished. Again, as far as I know, the analytic theory of numbers, as such, has led to no practical consequences. Yet one must think hard and long to find examples like this; and in so thinking, one is led to recognize that this is not quite the point. These great intellectual developments, whether they will in time lead to practical application or not, are continuous with and contiguous to parts of science which have played an enormous part in practice. The same methods as are developed in these fields are part of the equipment of the trained physical scientist; the same people who work in these fields may themselves be involved in practical affairs, or may be the teachers and colleagues of those who are. These circumstances derive from the fact that between all parts of science, even those which seem to us remote and unlike, there is a pervasive potential mutual relevance, a relevance often somewhat overdescribed as the unity of science.

Even if it were determined that only such new knowledge should be sought as would have practical consequences, or that only such studies should be supported by public funds, we should be poorly put to it to know how to carry out such decisions. We are in general not very good at imagining what will be the practical consequences of enquiry. We cannot be, because if the enquiry is well conceived it will not merely come up with a new answer; it will come up with something far more valuable, which is a new question, one which had not been thought of before. Out of such questions, and their progeny, the growth of science and the growth of practice both arise.

I should, of course, bitterly resist any limitation of science to that which is potentially useful; and it is clear to me that no very helpful limitation of this kind can in practice be applied. It is therefore fortunate, as other speakers will surely establish, that the costs of studying nature, in whatever appropriate form and in all its branches, are so extraordinarily modest, compared

7

to the costs, and in many cases we hope the value, of the practical developments based on such study. We may remember that Rutherford, who first understood nuclear transmutations, and who first induced them experimentally, held the then not unreasonable view that no practical use would be found on earth for nuclear energy.

We see in the great industrial societies of our time a very rapid and massive exploitation of new knowledge for practical ends. It would seem that there have been other cultures and other societies which did not act so, in which discoveries were unexploited for centuries. The example of which we have all been taught, not quite accurately, is the Chinese discovery of gunpowder, whose use was limited by them to pyrotechnics. I have some sympathy with the many who say that we should have followed their example in our dealings with the discovery of nuclear fission. But that is not for our time or style, nor is it likely to be for the changing emerging societies of the coming century. Most elaborate and beautiful mathematical methods were developed in Sumer and Babylon, which were initially responsive to the practical needs of the time: the prediction of eclipses, of conjunctions and first risings. These relatively advanced methods, which had, it is true, no element of kinematics or dynamics, seem to have been pursued for the love of technique and knowledge and virtuosity, and never to have been applied to any of the other problems for which they were suited.

In our world we will do something with new knowledge. The American Philosophical Society was founded for "the promotion of useful knowledge," and the Royal Society, its predecessor, had, in the words of its historian Thomas Sprat, a related purpose:

> Their Purpose is, in short, to make faithful *Records* of all the Works of *Nature,* or *Art,* which can come within their Reach; that so the present Age, and Posterity, may be able to put a Mark

8

on the Errors, which have been strengthened by long Prescription; to restore the Truths, that have lain neglected; to push on those, which are already known, to more various Uses; and to make the way more passable, to what remains unreveal'd.

The difference in emphasis between the English and the American versions reflects a real difference as to the temper and intention of the two cultures. In neither is there doubt that new knowledge will be used; in neither is there an expression of trouble as to how it should be.

The argument that the quest for new knowledge, which is basic science, is ennobling, and the argument that the quest for new knowledge produces new knowledge which is useful to technology and thus to practice, are disturbingly separate and unrelated arguments. They come from two worlds. In Göttingen in its high days there was a story told of Hilbert, the purest of mathematicians and one of the greatest. He had a colleague, Klein, who regarded mathematics as built upon practical problems, and as appropriately disciplined by the questions of natural science and technology. Klein would take some of his students to the technical high school at Hanover for a joint meeting, and they would talk there of their common problems. One year he was ill, and asked Hilbert to go in his stead and to say a few words against the then prevailing notion that basic science and technology stood in a hostile relationship to one another. To this Hilbert gladly agreed; but when he started to speak, his audience heard him say, "One hears a good deal nowadays about the hostility between science and technology. But that is not true, ladies and gentlemen. That is not true at all. How could it be true? They have nothing whatsoever to do with each other."

Yet science and technology are symbiotic. I suppose that our concern in these meetings is that this symbiosis be benign for both. They are symbiotic not only because technology would

9

be impoverished, blinded, and crippled were it not for the new knowledge which is sought and found for other reasons. Technology gives back again to science a rich reward in new instruments, new techniques, and new powers. Some of the largest questions that today agitate our curiosity and wonder relate to the disposition and motion of the remotest nebulae, billions of light years away. For evidence on this we look increasingly to radioastronomy, which is based on microwave techniques, largely developed for military purposes during and since World War II. Chemistry and biochemistry are able to put and answer questions not only of structure but of dynamics, because they have available the neutrons and tracers which, in large measure, are a byproduct of the industrial and military development of nuclear fission. It is this incessant feedback and reciprocal fertilization which makes a sharp distinction between pure science and technology academic and dreary. There is also an important traffic, not only in ideas and in equipment and in techniques, but in men, between the two, a traffic without which both would be the poorer. Indeed, the great lesson of the last decades has been that men of science who have spent their whole lives in the quest for new knowledge may be among the most gifted practitioners of technology.

Fermi came to the Los Alamos laboratory rather late, since he had great responsibilities in seeing that the new reactors at Oak Ridge and Hanford were in order. Shortly after he came, he expressed to me some astonishment that so large a proportion of the men in the laboratory, whom he had known in universities and seminars, were now more concerned with the practical problems of bomb design than with the larger questions of physics. Many kept that concern and those that developed from it; many returned to the university and the classroom; and of course, as in all large laboratories, there were some—some of the very best—who maintained throughout an independent curiosity, independent of bombs and all such matters. Out of this came, among many other things, the interest in controlled nuclear fusion and a new idea for the design of particle accelerators which has changed the history of fundamental physics. It is probable that no laboratory should ever be so dedicated to its practical mission or missions that it cannot afford a reasonable proportion—perhaps a sixth or a fifth—of work that is on the face of it unrelated to its purposes.

It may be good to recognize that new techniques and new resources are a better guide to new knowledge than a newly sense practical urgency. In general it may be wise also to recognize without equivocation, and without trying to soften it, the rather harsh disparity in the nature of, and the tension between, the two sets of reasons for encouraging the quest for new knowledge. It constitutes no new problem. Here is what Hobbes had to say:

> The Sciences, are small Power; because not eminent; and therefore, not acknowledged in any man; nor at all, but in a few; and in them, but of a few things. For Science is of that nature, as none can understand it to be, but such as in a good measure have attayned it.
>
> Arts of publique use, as Fortification, making of Engines, and other Instruments of War; because they conferre to Defence, and Victory, are Power: And though the true Mother of them, be Science, namely the Mathematiques; yet, because they are brought into the Light, by the hand of the Artificer, they be esteemed (the Midwife passing with the vulgar for the Mother) as his issue.

To the question, "Why do we need new knowledge?" we have heard two answers. One is that the search for it is ennobling; the other is that it offers man larger choices. The two answers, alas, suggest two further questions: "Ennobling for whom?" "By whom and how well are the choices made?"

There were societies in the past in which neither of these questions would have seemed difficult. Their difficulty today derives in part from the great growth of knowledge; it derives in part from the very great changes in the world which technology has brought about. These have combined to weaken and emasculate the public sector of our life, the sector which in past societies has been the seat of politics, art, religious practice, and the general sense of common purpose, and which encompassed the common elements of knowledge, myth, and sensibility. I contrast this public presence, not with the individual alone, nor with the family, but with something else, and in itself quite good. We live most social lives, and few of us can complain of solitude. We are banded together in communities and guilds of great variety and varying purpose: members of a profession, part of a corporation, inhabitants of a suburb. As a consequence, a great deal that is known to one of us is not known to another, and much even of what is known to all men of science is not present in the public life.

All of us know some of the ways in which this has come about. The rapidity with which knowledge grows makes it hard for professional men to be aware of all that is new in their own fields. The instrumental and traditional character of the new knowledge, based so largely on the accumulated skill and learning of the past, makes its transmission to others in other communities difficult, arduous, and time-consuming, or else sadly superficial and even misleading. The vastness of our society and its cherished inclusiveness have complicated all problems of communication, and have limited in a cruel way the healing help of friendship in uniting disparate arts and skills and insights. There are many other reasons, surely many of which I am not adequately aware. Surely we should not estimate too lightly the damaging effect, on the quality of public life, of having so large a part of knowledge alienated from public understanding and discourse, giving to the common life no insight, no confidence, no pleasure, no beauty. Communication is not a luxury in our lives; it is the basis of our humanity.

New knowledge should ennoble not merely those who seek and find it, nor their immediate colleagues; it should add to the civility and wonder and the nobility of the common life. This is no easy thing. We all know that we will go through our days ignorant of much that would be good for us to learn. We all accept the partialness of what we know well, and the deceptiveness and superficiality of what we know barely. Even the European tradition, with its regard for high intellectual vigor, long nurtured in more limited, more eclectic societies, is not up to coping with today's world. It has contributed to the uneven but major renascence of science in Russia.

I do not know how much can be done to restore the balance between what is known to some of us, and what is a part of a common culture; but it should not be by our default that we leave things as they are, nor for any lack of vigor in developing the manifold, difficult, partial remedies. They all rest on our fulfilling, as best we can, and in one of the many different senses of the word, our role as teachers—as lovers of new knowledge, who would share with all who will, of our generation and of the next, the wonders and the insights to which we have been led.

The many choices that new knowledge opens up for us are, in any society, made on many different levels and by many different men and institutions. Here we welcome this pluralism, and rightly see in it important safeguards from tyranny. Some are made by the management of a factory, some by a school board, some by a town council, some by a consumer, some by a worker or director in a laboratory. Yet all are made in the light of a general common understanding of the situation in which we find ourselves, and of what is good and bad. Some, which are importantly affected by the public interest, and which are among the gravest, must be made in the public sector, and by public institutions. This life that we have in common has had its cognitive basis weakened and debilitated because so much is missing from our common understanding, and from public knowledge. It is confronted with situations in many ways unlike those for which its institutions were devised and developed. Our public life is more vast; its events occur with a more startling variety and rapidity; and its interconnections are more numerous, more swift, more subtle, and less well understood than in any other age. It lacks, as an essential element of nobility, the union of simplicity and truth.

When the industrial revolution led to the increasingly widespread exploitation of fossil fuels, the public interest was ill protected, at least in part because the new knowledge required was not available. It developed without informed consideration of the grave future problems of health, of climate, and of the restructuring of human patterns of life. Even with the early development of nuclear fuels for industry, in spite of important and troublesome areas of continuing ignorance, we knew and know far more of the dangers and are far better prepared to cope with the public interest; but even of the knowledge that we do have, the part that is properly in the public sector, and is commonly understood, reveals a piteous lack of preparation for understanding it, and a strange and troubling mixture of exaggerated fear, hope, and pervasive cynicism.

Among the choices for which our inherited institutions appear poorly suited and inadequate are the uses of the unprecedented new instruments of warfare. Throughout history, arms have characteristically been the last arbiter of disputes. We have come to live in an age when this cannot continue. Yet political institutions, if they are to serve man at all, can probably not change at the rate at which our technical society is changing, or in any way match the growth in our knowledge of nature. I have not been able to conceive, nor have I heard, of any development of national or international institutions which is at the same time adequate to meet these new problems and which yet has any touch at all of human or historical plausibility. Thus, as we all know, we live very close to the edge of disaster.

I believe most simply in the nobility of this great effort to understand nature, and what we can of ourselves, that is science. I hope, less simply, that it may yet be a brave and worthy chapter of man's history to cope, with a full awareness of the frailty of his institutions, of his society, and of himself, with the new problems and new choices that this knowledge has opened. For if we do not treasure the great inheritance on which all our work and life are based, and understand the radical novelty and the gravity of the situation in which we find ourselves, there will be few of our children to ask again of the need for new knowledge.

Basic Research in the
UNITED STATES

ALAN T. WATERMAN
National Science Foundation

THE TOPIC that has been assigned to me, "Basic Research in the United States," is generous, indeed, in its scope. It is reminiscent of a communication from an early correspondent of the National Science Foundation, who dropped us a postcard requesting simply: "Please send me everything you have on science." Since we planned that this symposium be devoted to a detailed discussion of the various aspects of basic research in this country, I have viewed my own role as being primarily one of establishing a general framework within which this topic will be discussed. I propose, therefore, to describe rather briefly our aims in basic research as I see them, the manner in which such research is carried on, the sources from which it derives support, and the role of the federal government in relation to what is now clearly a major national resource.

Early Basic Research

To speak of research in the United States raises the immediate question: What are its distinguishing characteristics? In what respects, if any, is it different from research being carried on in other parts of the world? Are there any essential differences between the aims, techniques, or general philosophy of our research people and those of other nations?

I believe it would generally be agreed that our academic traditions of research closely resemble those of Europe. This is a powerful and noble tradition strongly fostered by scientific societies, by the academies of science in many countries, and by international cooperation through such bodies as the scientific unions. Happily, one can say with great assurance that the time-honored tradition of soundness and integrity of research has been upheld throughout the world. All have shared in the growth of its techniques, both theoretical and experimental.

There are signs, perhaps, that as more and more of our people receive their training wholly in this country we may be developing patterns of our own. Certainly the high prestige that has long been accorded science by our leading technical industries and their rapid development under this philosophy bears an American imprint. In any event, the most pronounced difference between research in the United States and in most other countries has probably been its encouragement among our industries and the extensive participation of scientists and engineers employed by industry.

Another distinguishing characteristic that can be ascribed to our national research effort is its scope and variety. Research is being actively pursued in industry, in private, commercial, and government laboratories, and, above all, in a bewildering variety of educational institutions, both public and private, large and small. Furthermore, nature has endowed us generously with a wide variety of natural resources which, in fields such as zoology, botany, forestry, geology, and many aspects of geophysical research, afford natural laboratories for the study of nature. We undoubtedly have greater financial resources than most countries for the support of scientific research, provided we choose to make them available. Whether or not we are making a wise or sufficient apportionment of these financial resources is a critical issue for this symposium. For purposes of generalization, however, one may say that research in the United States differs from research in other countries chiefly in its diversity and volume. This may not be entirely true in comparison with the USSR, whose natural resources in many ways compete with our own, and whose present drive for scientific and technical accomplishment represents a major challenge.

One more distinguishing characteristic of US research as a whole should be mentioned: the nation's emphasis upon applied science—"inventions"—and its outstanding success in technology. This characteristic was early observed by de Tocqueville:

> In America the purely practical part of science is admirably understood, and careful attention is paid to the theoretical portion which is immediately requisite to application. On this head the Americans always display a clear, free, original, and inventive power of mind. But scarcely any one in the United States devotes himself to the essentially theoretical and abstract portion of human knowledge. . . . These very Americans, who have not discovered one of the general laws of mechanics, have introduced into navigation an engine which changes the aspect of the world. . . .

Within the past thirty years or so, however, our strength and interest in basic research have grown until now one hears the words on everyone's lips. In fact, one worries lest through over-use "basic research" lose its main impact. It is well to bear in mind the Athenian statesman Aristides, who lost an election simply because people were tired of hearing him called "The Just."

The term "basic research" first received general recognition when used by Vannevar Bush in the well-known report,

Science, the Endless Frontier, which he was asked to make by President Roosevelt. In that report, Bush said "Basic research is performed without thought of practical ends. . . . [It] leads to new knowledge. It provides scientific capital." Indeed, in my opinion, the following statement from the same source probably sums up admirably the purpose for which this symposium was called:

> . . . it is important to emphasize that there is a perverse law governing research: Under the pressure for immediate results, and unless deliberate policies are set up to guard against this, *applied research invariably drives out pure.*
>
> The moral is clear: It is pure research which deserves and requires special protection and specially assured support.

In fact, it is this Bush analogue of Gresham's law which, in my belief, underlies and makes essential special emphasis upon basic research, by whatever name it is called. The original name given to basic research was usually "pure," which had obviously unfortunate connotations. The definition used by the National Science Foundation in its fact-gathering surveys has been:

> Basic research is that type of research which is directed toward increase of knowledge in science. It is research where the primary aim of the investigator is a fuller knowledge or understanding of the subject under study, rather than a practical application thereof.

This definition has stood the test of time fairly well. One objection commonly heard, however, is: How can one determine the investigator's motives? The simplest answer is that if one feels he must make a psychiatric test of an individual to determine why he wants to do a piece of research, then it is undoubtedly basic.

Beginning of Government Support

Although basic research has been cultivated in the United States for many decades, its growth did not particularly accelerate until the period following World War I. There are, perhaps, historical reasons for this. Brooke Hindle, in his book, *The Pursuit of Science in Revolutionary America,* observes:

> With respect to science, there was serious question whether America could support scientific work of the sort Franklin demanded in 1743. Nowhere in the colonies could be found the rich libraries, the ancient universities, or the conversation of the learned that graced the centers of Old World culture. Great endowed institutions were lacking. So, for the most part, was the patronage of the king and of enlightened nobles. Stimulus and support from Europe could supply only a part of the deficiency. Communication was slow and uncertain and the encouragement offered was not balanced but biased by the particular needs of the individuals who offered it. Development of a fruitful scientific life demanded far more of the people and the society that sought it than did the successful practice of self-government. As Dr. Thomas Bond later remarked, "[Science] is a child of a thousand Years—Approaches slowly to Maturity, and is long in dying."

In this passage, the key word is "patronage." The advancement of knowledge has always required patronage. Many of the early scientists were men of wealth and position who supported their own studies out of their private purses. Those less fortunately situated required the patronage of king or noble.

In a republic such as the United States, this form of patronage was lacking, and the universities and colleges, which were the only institutions equipped to do research, derived support from their respective states or from endowments, according to whether they were public or private institutions. The notion of the federal government supporting scientific research came much later. A question for our own times is: To what extent should basic research be supported out of tax funds and to what extent by industrial firms, endowment funds, and other sources of private support?

Once the idea of government support took hold, it gained momentum, and today a little less than half of all the basic research in the United States is being supported out of federal funds. This brings us to the reasons why the federal government supports research. The principal official reason is, in general, to advance the national health, security, and welfare. This is formal language—the language of charters. Nevertheless, it is fundamental and enlightening. It is an admission that science can "advance the national health, security, and welfare," but the implication is that only to the extent that science makes identifiable contributions to the public good should it be supported by the federal government.

Basis of Government Support

At this point some confusion arises. The "charter" language is clearly justification for federal support of directed or applied research—how can it, however, justify support of *basic* research, especially under the definition just stated? It is present government policy, with which I heartily agree, that government support of basic research is indeed justified, even though the primary objective of the investigator may be solely a fuller understanding of the subject under study. In fact, the National Science Foundation was responsible for specific policy on this point, stated in an Executive Order of the President in 1954:

> . . . the Foundation shall be increasingly responsible for providing support by the Federal Government for general-purpose basic research through contracts and grants. The conduct and support by other Federal agencies of basic research in areas which are closely related to their missions is recognized as important and desirable, especially in response to current national needs, and shall continue.

The best statement in explanation of this point of view that I know of is contained in a report on basic research made by a Department of Defense committee, of which Warren Weaver was Chairman:

It is essential to recognize that there are two aspects of basic research, depending upon who is viewing it.

From the point of view of the research worker himself basic research is research motivated by curiosity and interest, carried out because it promises to add to knowledge, and without any necessary interest in or concern for the practical applicability of any results that may be obtained.

Nevertheless it is most strikingly and emphatically true that basic research is not impractical research. The whole history of science constitutes a most impressive proof of this statement. And a research administrator, informed as to the history of research and aware of the interrelationships between various fields of science and various fields of application, can, concerning a given body of basic research activity, reasonably make judgments concerning probable practicality, these being judgments which may be quite foreign if not meaningless to the individuals actually doing the research.

Thus it is quite obvious if one is interested in, say, the development of new materials which will maintain strength at high temperatures, that there are certain areas of pure research which have probable relevance to such problems, and other areas which are clearly unlikely to yield results useful for this purpose.

Thus, without in any way abandoning or contradicting the concept of basic research as viewed by the researcher, the research administrator can discriminate between various areas of basic research, and can sensibly judge that certain of these general areas have a high probability of producing results useful for given purposes, while others have a very low probability. In other words, having a field of application in mind, it is meaningful and sensible for a research administrator, without in any way influencing the creative atmosphere within which the researcher himself operates, to judge that certain areas of basic research have, with high probability, relevance to his practical interests.

What I have just said applies to any typical government agency with a practical mission, such as defense or health. But in justifying basic research on these grounds, as government support grows, one soon gets an uneasy feeling that all will not be well with science throughout the nation if government supports basic research *only* for such practical reasons. Mind you, I do not wish to criticize the need for support on these grounds—it is very great indeed—but this principle will certainly cause fields of science to be neglected where the connection with immediate practical objectives is not so obvious. Furthermore, there is a philosophical objection which in the long-run may outweigh the one just stated. In time there may be danger that science will come to be regarded only as a means to practical ends. Such motivation is short-sighted and makes ever more remote the chance of fundamental, completely novel discovery in science. History is very convincing on this point.

How then can the difficulty be resolved? It can be done—by considering basic research as an investment. Since basic research is exploration into the unknown, the degree of success any single piece of research may achieve is uncertain. Support must therefore be planned and carried out over a wide range of subjects. Then, statistically, one may be assured of a high return on a fair percentage of the work undertaken. In practice, one may even state with some confidence that the return on this small percentage far more than pays the cost of the entire investment. The analogy can be carried further. One should invest in daring projects that appear to have small chance of succeeding but a big pay-off if they do. And there should be a fair proportion of standard gilt-edge projects that promise a small but reliable return. In this way, one can manage to include all fields of basic research, and in so doing feel happy to have found an approach that appeals to budget-minded citizens.

Nevertheless, the fact remains that, in this country especially, we have not yet reached the point where we can step forth boldly and justify basic research in terms of its important objective, namely, the pursuit of knowledge for its own sake—

as typified by the work of Galileo, Newton, Maxwell, Faraday, Henry, Darwin, Gibbs, and Einstein. Until we are willing to acknowledge and indeed proclaim the importance of purely intellectual and spiritual goals, I am convinced that we shall never realize the full advantages of basic research. If this point of view is correct, then something must be done to change public attitudes or we are in for a gradual but increasing erosion of the quality of our science. This in turn inevitably reacts upon the quality of our technological performance (for those who stress the practical side). More importantly, I suspect our attitude here can subtly affect our whole philosophy.

Surely one of the great assets of a democracy is the encouragement of individual initiative. This should certainly be true in the field of intellectual endeavor as well as in other fields. It is a curious anomaly, however, that we who regard ourselves as the leading exponents of democracy do not seem to respect this principle in intellectual activities to the same extent that many other nations do. It is not enough that our scientific and political leaders should subscribe to this principle; a respect for learning, intellectual prowess, must characterize our people as a whole. Otherwise, the encouragement of intellectual activity, and indeed creative activity of all kinds, will never enjoy a proper measure of significant and lasting support. In science, nature will become an opponent to be overcome, rather than a friend to be won for the enrichment of our lives.

Basic Research versus Research and Development

Let us turn now to the organizational pattern under which basic research is conducted in this country. Some general understanding of these matters is essential if we are to consider the problems confronting basic research at the present time. According to National Science Foundation studies for the year

1956-57, the most recent for which we have complete information, out of $9 billion total for research and development in the United States, some $670 million, or more than 7 per cent, is going for the support of basic research. It should be borne in mind, moreover, that this amount covers all sorts of costs including the operation of expensive research "tools" such as nuclear particle accelerators, research rockets, and radiotelescopes. Of the total, the federal government is the source of $320 million, or 48 per cent; industry $225 million, or 33 per cent; the universities and other nonprofit institutions $125 million, or 19 per cent.

Another index to the relative proportion of effort among the principal sponsors of basic research is the number of scientists and engineers engaged in these activities. As is well known, many scientists and engineers combine research and development with other pursuits such as teaching or industrial production. If we simply add up the amount of time given to research and development activities by all our scientists and engineers, we find that this amounts to the equivalent of about 300,000 full-time researchers, or about a quarter of the total number of scientists and engineers. Of the 300,000 full-time equivalents in research and development, about 27,000 are in basic research, or about 9 per cent.

Our estimates indicate, further, that the largest number of basic research scientists, 14,000, or slightly over one-half, are employed in educational and other nonprofit institutions; the second largest number, 9000, or one-third, are working in industry; and the remaining 4000 (15 per cent) in the federal government.

The University

The university has for many years been the traditional home of basic research. Ideally, it is here that the so-called

26

uncommitted investigator, in an atmosphere of academic freedom, can pursue his individual researches without reference
to practical objectives. In recent years, however, the universities have been subjected to new pressures in the form of the
government's need for a wide variety of so-called contract
research. In both the scientific community and the federal
government, concern has been expressed lest outside demands
for the solution of pressing practical problems jeopardize the
university's traditional role of education and free research. The
National Science Foundation found it desirable to make a
special study of the situation, which was published last year
under the title, "Government-University Relationships in Fed-
erally Sponsored Scientific Research and Development." This
study notes that:

> In certain specialized fields, such as engineering, agriculture,
> and medicine, applied research is frequently closely related to
> educational objectives. Federal support of applied research projects
> in these fields appears to present no fundamental problem in terms
> of interference with the traditional functions of colleges and uni-
> versities. However, with such exceptions noted, . . . Federal agen-
> cies [should] consider other alternatives before establishing large-
> scale applied research and development projects (particularly those
> concerned with development and testing) within institutions of
> higher learning. Such alternatives would include: (*a*) Federal
> laboratories; (*b*) industrial or other private laboratories; and (*c*)
> research centers organizationally separated from the institution
> proper.

The question of preserving the basic research functions of
our universities is a fundamental one. So long as our universities are unable to obtain adequate funds for the support of
their normal activities, they may be tempted to supplement
their regular budgets by contract funds, and possibly in so
doing, to undertake projects and programs to meet needs other
than strictly scientific and educational. This means that teach-

27

ers and experienced research investigators needed for the guidance and training of future scientists may be diverted to urgent practical problems or away from a specialty of their free choice.

The problem is not as simple as it may seem. Public service is often mentioned as one of a university's aims, particularly training for public service; state universities, especially, cannot neglect this responsibility. One of our first problems, therefore, is to see that our universities, both private and state, are adequately supported, in order that they may plan and carry out the educational and research programs that they really want, accepting or declining bids for research according to their ability to perform it without disruption of the university's normal program.

But let us try to be fair and objective about these matters and not cling blindly to tradition. It may be that in the modern university all disciplines should begin to follow the lead of agriculture and medicine and cultivate the applicational side. This is a point to be considered carefully, however, since we should do this with our eyes open and with proper safeguards for the strength and well-being of free basic research. My own thought is that the growing practical applications of physics, chemistry, and mathematics should be shifted to engineering departments and kept out of the regular science departments, much as applied biology belongs in medical schools.

Industrial Laboratories

Although the conservation of basic research as an activity of our universities is most certainly a primary consideration at the present time, other means for the advancement of basic research merit consideration. During the past ten years, the amount of basic research in industrial laboratories has increased; but if our total basic research effort is not to lag behind

28

the demands of applied research and development, industry's participation and contributions must continue to increase.

It should be noted, also, that the years since the war have marked the rise of new organizational forms for the furtherance of basic research. These include research centers, such as the national laboratories, of which Los Alamos, Argonne, and Brookhaven are major examples, and are run by a university, a group of universities, or an industrial concern, under contract to the federal government. In general they are engaged in both basic and applied research, where considerations of both cost and security have dictated that the work be carried on under direct government sponsorship.

More recently, groups of universities have begun to collaborate in similar fashion for the conduct of basic research in other fields. In the field of astronomy, for example, the National Science Foundation is supporting two major projects: the radio astronomy facility being constructed and operated at Green Bank, West Virginia, by Associated Universities, Inc., and the optical astronomy facility on Kitt Peak, in Tucson, Arizona, being constructed and operated by the Association of Universities for Research in Astronomy, Inc. A recent group to enter the field is the University Committee for Atmospheric Research, organized by a group of fourteen universities. This group is proposing to the National Science Foundation the establishment of a national institute to do basic research in the atmospheric sciences. The proposal is the result of a recommendation made last year by the Committee on Meteorology, of the National Academy of Sciences-National Research Council.

It is clear that certain broad fields, such as astronomy, atmospheric research, oceanography, materials, and space research, lend themselves well to cooperative effort. The research institute has for many years been a highly successful establishment in a number of European countries, notably Germany,

29

USSR, and Sweden. It is practically certain that the expanding horizon of research in this country will dictate the organization of new forms of research activity here. In the first place, there will continue to be pressures for organized attack upon critical, practical problems, of both basic and applied nature, such as that which currently obtains with respect to materials. Whether these needs can best be met by the establishment of special centers for the purpose, or whether coordinated programs should be set up in more decentralized fashion will be a matter for consideration in each case. In the second place, the voice of science itself will come increasingly to be heard demanding support for highly significant areas of science, mainly basic.

A word of caution is in order here. We must, of course, be alert to the trends of the future and do justice to concerted efforts in science, but we must also be alert to the weaknesses as well as the strengths inherent in massive and concentrated effort. Are we likely, for example, to overemphasize group activity at the expense of the individual researcher? Certainly history indicates that capital discoveries can usually be attributed to a single person or a few individuals, although it is quickly admitted that their particular contributions may be only the climax of a host of smaller research contributions which preceded theirs. Those who are familiar with group activities will probably agree, if they are candid, that the tendency of the group is to be conservative although powerful, and in its dedication to its objective, to react rather conservatively to radical ideas or subject matter lying on the periphery of its main activity. Furthermore, an organized group tends to achieve a singleness of purpose and of method which by its very nature is apt to ignore ideas from outside.

The large research center introduces another quite serious problem in the view of many. A unique bulwark of university research is admittedly the close association between graduate faculty and graduate students. How can a specialized research center or facility effectively collaborate with university research and graduate education? If within the university, it tends to monopolize attention; if remote from the university, it suffers from inaccessibility. Although we do not wish to overlook the strength of an organized group for attacking broad and complex problems, neither must we neglect to encourage and back individuals and smaller groups who may approach the subject from other disciplines or other points of view. The question seems to me to be an important one of the desirable balance between group and individual effort, certainly in basic research. Above all, we should not try to claim that either alternative has sole merit.

Independent Research Groups

We have mentioned the universities, private industry, and the federal government as engaged, in varying degrees, in the conduct of basic research. A further significant category includes the independent, nonprofit laboratories and institutes established or enlarged in recent decades to satisfy a research need not completely served by governmental, industrial, commercial, and educational facilities. The independent research laboratories consist generally of those that control their own incomes from endowment funds, and those that derive the bulk of their income from contracts or grants, most commonly from the federal government.

The independent research institutes and laboratories account for the smallest share of national expenditures for research and development but they are making a significant contribution to the advancement of knowledge. The report of the President's Science Advisory Committee, issued last December under the title, "Strengthening American Science," underscores the role of private initiative in the support of basic research. The report comments:

> There is also a vital and unique role for private foundations to play in supporting imaginative and audacious research that industry or Government may not always support. Relatively modest sums, wisely expended, can still underwrite and stimulate creative scientific work of the first order. Private foundations can also stimulate the growth of more first-rate scientific institutions, and cultivate in them the intellectual climate indispensable to high scholarship.

One cannot leave this subject without paying full tribute to the outstanding contributions to basic as well as applied research made by the research laboratories of a number of technical industries and of the government, and to the increasing amount of good work done by a variety of special independent research and development groups.

This cursory review of the various organizational entities by which basic research is carried on in the United States will serve to illustrate the extent to which we enjoy diversity in this country in our approach to the research effort. This is good. After all, research in science is a human activity carried on by men. Therefore, it will necessarily have all the complexities and subtleties that human beings have. Thus there is not, and never can be, any standard manner of conducting research. The method may be systematic, thorough, painstaking; or it may be erratic, inspirational, and highly individual. This truth is one of the great strengths of science.

The Federal Government

I turn now to my final topic, which is a quick glance at the role of the federal government in relation to the research effort. During the last several decades we have witnessed a technological revolution that has had vast impact on our daily lives, profoundly influenced relationships among nations, and now bids fair literally to take us out of this world in pursuit of new and exciting objectives. The lack of financial support from private sources for basic research, particularly in the nation's universities, has forced the government to fill the gap. The government finds itself in the role of both performer and supporter of basic research, and many agencies conduct and support basic research related to their over-all missions. Such agencies include, principally, the Department of Defense, Atomic Energy Commission, the National Aeronautics and Space Administration, National Institutes of Health, Department of Agriculture, Departments of Commerce and Interior.

Until a few years ago, the federal funds available for the support of uncommitted research in the universities were small indeed. It was to meet this need that the National Science Foundation was established in 1950 to support and encourage basic research and education in the sciences. The new agency was also directed to "develop and encourage the pursuit of a national policy for the promotion of basic research and education in the sciences."

The Foundation has deliberately continued the policy initiated by the Office of Naval Research and observed generally throughout the government of providing support to the basic research that is regarded as most promising and significant by the scientists in their respective fields. With the collaboration of the country's scientists, a national program* has been developed that is directed primarily and simply toward progress in science. In principle, such a program, developed as it is in consultation with the leading research specialists of the country,

* One exception to this form of extramural support is the long-established program of the Department of Agriculture, which provides matching funds for state agricultural research.

33

represents the most authoritative judgment available toward significant progress in research. Furthermore, this means of developing research programs for federal support is backed by the majority of the country's research scientists.

Following this policy, during the last decade and a half, a sizable and reasonably stable program of federal support for basic research has been established, primarily in colleges and universities and other nonprofit institutions. Does this effectively meet the current needs of science? One answer to this question has grown increasingly clear in recent years: Although the federal support program as thus developed has the advantages mentioned, and although it provides for the support needed by individuals and groups who carry on the research, it does not recognize adequately the needs of science departments of educational institutions as such. In order to obtain a well-balanced program in support of science, one must consider the following: (a) the progress of research in science; (b) the development of the individual scientist; (c) the health and growth of the institutions where science is taught and where research is done. Present federal policy, by the support of faculty members and graduate students via research grants and contracts, emphasizes the first of these—progress in scientific research. Through fellowship programs, both predoctoral and postdoctoral, and by directing attention to the teaching and content of scientific courses, the federal government contributes to the second, the development of the individual. But with the exception of state universities through the Department of Agriculture, and medical schools through the National Institutes of Health, the broad needs of departments of science and engineering in the colleges and universities of the country are not being adequately provided for.

Initially, it was thought that federal support of research projects in educational institutions would free a portion of their funds for general coverage in science. Gradually, however, as the scope of federal research programs increased, the volume of federal support to many institutions has disturbed the normal balance of research and has caused financial strain through government failure to pay full costs.

At the present time, outstanding needs exist that are not being met. Chief among these is the need for new or renovated laboratories, for research and teaching equipment and facilities, and, in certain fields, for costly modern research installations. On top of this is the ever mounting cost of maintenance. The situation appears to call for general aid to United States universities patterned somewhat after that provided universities in the United Kingdom by the University Grants Committee. In any event, the question arises of direct subsidy to educational institutions in order to increase the over-all strength of their departments and to provide greater flexibility in their administration.

Now, direct financial assistance to academic departments or institutions raises a serious policy question: Should the federal government break precedent and provide direct aid to higher education in the fields of science? Can this be done without danger of loss of independence of the institutions supported? Can this be done wisely and acceptably by selective support in the manner of the current research support, or should it be done universally according to some suitable formula? Presumably, an obvious safeguard would be the provision for matching funds. Then there is the complicating factor of two primary classes of institutions: public and private. Despite the difficulties, however, it is quite clear that the needs are real and urgent. The responsibility of the federal government is to learn the facts, point out the problem and its urgency, and see that effective action is taken. In my opinion, this means consideration both of ways of assisting state and

35

MILLS COLLEGE
LIBRARY

private sources to meet the need (through such measures as revision of the tax structure), and of ways and means of providing some degree of direct support.

In the meantime, I believe that history will discover that the government's role in relation to research and development has on the whole been an enlightened one. In its broad attack on the degenerative and crippling diseases that afflict mankind; in its development and exploitation of nuclear energy for peaceful purposes; in its support of basic research unrelated to practical objectives—the government's efforts have contributed greatly to the general welfare. In charting the way through a new field of activity for which precedents and experience were generally lacking, there have, of course, been mistakes and errors of judgment. Nevertheless, as one who has been associated with government research for nearly two decades, I can say that it has shown vitality, flexibility, and the capacity to meet changing needs and situations. Also it has not encroached directly upon the independence of individual scientists and groups supported. For example, federal support of research at colleges and universities exists in various forms ranging from the very narrow to the very broad. The operations of current forms of support are continually studied with a view to adopting modifications and alternatives that would improve the environment for basic research without at the same time being subject to abuse. All forms of support, both narrow and broad, appear to have their place in the general pattern of federal support. In the Foundation, we feel that each agency should use those forms best suited to particular needs at a particular time and should be free to vary its general pattern whenever desirable.

We are striving to assure stability and continuity of support by awarding grants for longer terms; and there has also been an effort to liberalize, as much as possible, reporting requirements and accountability for research equipment. The government is quite aware that research and development efforts, whether by contract or through grant, cannot and should not be regulated and administered like a procurement contract, for example. It is worth noting that recently the Congress has provided authority to all federal agencies to make grants for basic research and also to transfer title to equipment provided under basic research grants to the grantee.

Summary

In summary, research in the United States has great inherent strength and versatility, and, in comparison with other countries, is especially strong in industry-related programs. A nationwide program in support of basic research by the federal government has been established, aimed at progress in science along lines laid down by the scientists themselves. This program includes, as an important component, basic research in support of areas of research and development underlying the missions of individual federal agencies. Basic research is also conducted vigorously by a number of leading industries, many of which provide support to universities and other research establishments, chiefly in areas of interest to them. Colleges and universities continue to constitute the principal centers of basic research activity.

The evidence is, however, that basic research in the United States should be more strongly supported at colleges and universities, in order to strengthen our future technology by the progress made on the frontiers of science, in order to retain highly competent staff, and to assure high quality training of a great number of young scientists and engineers.

Outstanding problems to be met include: provision for renovation of research laboratories, provision of up-to-date scientific equipment for research and instruction at colleges and universities, and a solution to the problem of science-department support at educational institutions, which is needed to balance the volume of basic research support provided selectively.

Among the most important issues of the future will undoubtedly be the needs and pressures for dealing with special areas of research, presently typified by atmospheric physics, oceanography, and materials research. In many of these areas, research will be required to help solve development problems, while in others it will be chiefly significant to the progress of science itself. The manner of handling these problems and the correlation and collaboration among industry, government, and universities will require careful thought. At present, the best strategy would seem to be the evaluation of each such proposal on its individual merits, and it is likely that a considerable degree of experimentation in administrative and organizational handling will be profitable.

The federal government is now better prepared than ever before for the consideration of such matters because, in addition to the interested departments and agencies, there is the new Federal Council for Science and Technology, recently established by the President; the Special Assistant to the President for Science and Technology, Dr. Killian, in the White House; and the very active President's Science Advisory Committee.

Responsibilities for science matters in the federal government can be described as follows: With respect to the role of the federal government in the support of basic research, the National Science Foundation with its National Science Board has the primary responsibility for dealing with policy concerning federal support of basic research throughout the country. The Federal Council for Science and Technology deliberates on matters of policy coordination and future planning among federal agencies and makes recommendations to the President.

The President's Science Advisory Committee, drawn from non-government scientists and engineers, considers important scientific and technical matters in relation to government policy, with special reference to national security. The presence in the White House of the Special Assistant to the President for Science and Technology makes available to the President at all times advice and counsel on the wide range of scientific and technical affairs.

In spite of the growth and strength of federal programs in research and development and the assets that have been described, it is clear that the potential of the country in science and technology is far from being realized. The element most requiring attention is a greater degree of support throughout the country for basic research and for the education and training of scientists and engineers. For this realization of our full potential there must be widespread public recognition, understanding, and appreciation of the importance of intellectual and scholarly activity, and the pursuit of excellence in all fields of intellectual endeavor. Only in this way will the country be able to engage successfully in world competition. Only in this way will our nation be capable of leadership and collaboration among the nations of the world in the vast new vistas which science is disclosing.

The most important and enduring element in basic research is still expressed in the trite phrase, "the pursuit of truth." This theme moves through the lives and works of our most outstanding men of science, arts, and letters. The creative instinct or urge, its integrity, its imaginative and constructive approach toward man's problems and aspirations undoubtedly represents the highest and noblest use of his talents, as stated so clearly by Bronowski in *Science and Human Values*:

> Whether our work is art or science or the daily work of society, it is only the form in which we explore our experience which is different; the need to explore remains the same. This is why, at

39

bottom, the society of scientists is more important than their discoveries. What science has to teach us here is not its techniques but its spirit: the irresistible need to explore . . . the inspiration of science for four hundred years has . . . created the values of our intellectual life and, with the arts, has taught them to our civilization. Science has nothing to be ashamed of even in the ruins of Nagasaki. The shame is theirs who appeal to other values than the human and imaginative values which science has evolved. The shame is ours if we do not make science part of our world, intellectually as much as physically, so that we may at last hold these halves of the world together by the same values. For it is the lesson of science that the concept is more profound than its laws, and the act of judging more critical than the judgment . . . "Poetry does not move us to be just or unjust, in itself. It moves us to thoughts in whose light justice and injustice are seen in fearful sharpness of outline." What is true of poetry is true of all creative thought. And what I said . . . of one value is true of all human values. The values by which we are to survive are not rules for just and unjust conduct, but are those deeper illuminations in whose light justice and injustice, good and evil, means and ends are seen in fearful sharpness of outline.

THE PARADOX
OF CHOICE

W. O. BAKER
Bell Telephone Laboratories

Introduction

THE PARADOX of choice for the research scientist is, of course, the choice between doing what his interests impel him to do and doing what some large part of society might seek to have done. A paradox is a statement or proposition which at first view seems absurd. A chief planner of this symposium on basic research has wisely seen that to make a scientist choose between the paths of his interest and the route of some institution's interest (which would most often be a route leading to immediate utility and the solving of the most urgent problems) presents a paradox. Fortunately, with equal wisdom this planner has realized that man has forever lived with paradoxes. We have only now to indicate how the scientific man may live with this paradox of choice and, by recognizing it, may enrich our nation's welfare and culture.

That mankind has lived with paradoxes and has adapted to their apparent contradictions is illustrated in the sixth chapter of Second Corinthians:

> As unknown, and yet well known;
> As dying, and behold, we live;

As chastened, and not killed;
As sorrowful, yet always rejoicing;
As poor, yet making many rich;
As having nothing, and yet possessing all things.

II Cor. 6:9, 10

As an aside, how majestically those last two lines describe the circumstances of the scholar and, further, the conditions of paradox of choice for the scientist and technologist. Such a condition was recognized about five hundred years ago by Roger Bacon's deep insight into the meaning of science and technology for civilization. He wrote:

> Now among all the benefits that could be conferred upon mankind I found none so great as the discovery of new arts, endowments and commodities for the bettering of man's life. For I saw that among the crude people in primitive homes that authors of inventions and discoveries were consecrated and numbered among the gods. . . .

With this high praise for the meaning of what we would now call applied research and engineering, Bacon went on, however, to represent what has been widely accepted in ensuing centuries as the pervading theme of true basic scientific research, that is, to gain understanding. He wrote:

> But above all, if a man could succeed, not in striking out some particular invention, however useful, but in kindling a light in nature—a light which should in its ray rising touch and illuminate all the border regions that confine upon the circle of our present knowledge; and so spreading further and further should presently disclose and bring into sight all that is most hidden and secret in the world, that man (I thought) would be the benefactor indeed of the human race—the propagator of man's empire over the universe, the champion of the liberty, the conqueror and subduer of necessities.

Here it sounds, particularly in the last phrases, as though Bacon had recognized not only the duality in the destiny of the scientific researcher in the centuries to come but also the paradox of choice that would confront that worker. The reason that choice seems to be involved is so familiar to scientists and scholars that it hardly needs saying again. It comes from the way man's mind works in his search for new knowledge and understanding. In that search, experience shows that the best scholar does just what he wants to do when and how he wants to do it. He is disciplined, of course, by his own will. However, the man working for practical ends, especially in collaboration with a group of others, must obviously adjust his thinking and acting to the common objectives and to the ways agreed upon to advance the group toward those objectives.

Industry and government must first identify their scientific missions. These are not necessarily their technical or engineering needs for a preconceived end product—a flexible glass or a solid propellant. We shall maintain presently that these missions usually can be identified truly only if there is a theoretical insight that tells a company what business of science it is in; unless and until a government or industry program has some theoretical science connected with it, it seems doubtful if a satisfactory situation for "relevant" basic research can obtain.

Finally, several examples will be cited where large new areas appear to be opening up in which the paradox of choice for the basic researcher can be maintained, in both industry and government.

From this point of view, we might look at resolving the paradox of choice in two principal ways. First, we could try to understand what makes the scholar and scientist want to do what he wants to do. Knowing this, perhaps those who conduct research *im grossem* would simply make it so that the finest and most creative minds would belong to particular egos. These would above all prefer to follow along certain cooperative,

43

orderly, routes toward a specific scientific or technical objective. They would, indeed, be said to be "highly motivated" to that end. But I think we will have to leave this operation to our neighbors on Madison Avenue. Most of them over there now have research departments, and some day they may find among their "hidden persuaders" ways to marshal research scientists in the fashion we have just discussed.

The second possibility for resolving the paradox recognizes that those having the ablest and most creative minds will prefer to use them in basic research by following up the undirected, uncontrolled, unspecified, unprogrammed, and certainly unknown courses revealed as the work itself goes ahead. These courses naturally multiply as basic research progresses in a particular field. It would be good even to know why a basic scientist takes one of the paths rather than another that seems to branch off from the same point. The remarkable thing is the high consistency with which genius in science seems over and over to take unerringly the right path from among many branches. Sometimes one thinks it is because the genius sees what he can do and avoids those choices of paths which would lead him into areas of tasks presently unfeasible or overwhelming. Anyway, it is recognized that this *modus vivendi* in basic research will not fit easily into some master pattern for acquiring a fast-selling cure for backache or for a weightless, endless electrical power source for a space vehicle. Industry and government should give up trying to program things this way. Therefore, we have somehow to present to the gifted researcher situations in which he will feel little or no inhibition of the free travel of the pathways of his mind. But at the same time there must be easily available to him, as a social as well as an intellectual creature, ways to see and to relate to the conditions described by Bacon. Then, we believe that many devices of modern technical organization can be brought in. These clear

44

the way to Bacon's paradoxical goal of the man who as "the conqueror and the subduer of necessities" is not the inventor, but one who is "kindling a light in Nature." They include such things as having development and engineering clearly separate from, but near to, research, in easing in all possible ways for rapid communication between these areas, and among the research people themselves, and many other systems which are nowadays well known, or at least well discussed.

However, there must also be things far deeper than these institutional and administrative conveniences. These things must affect the very culture of the scholar and basic researcher. In order to consider them, we must next think of the conditions in human affairs under which basic scientific research has evolved. We should discuss a bit the relation of the highly personalized intellect noted above to human values and to human wants generally. After some thought on that, we shall try to propose some ways in which the institutions of society, having definite needs and aims for the use of science, can nevertheless provide conditions of choice highly favorable to the success and satisfaction of the individual scientist. But even the pressure to make such choice has been relatively slow in coming. The asking of society for basic research has, of course, been until now minuscule (or less?). Indeed, the trivial interest of civilization at large in basic scientific research is sometimes hard to realize in the technical frenzy of our present time. Perhaps it takes the detachment of the philosopher to remind us scientists of where we really stand in human affairs. George Santayana said:

> Science . . . has flourished only twice in recorded times, once for some 300 years in ancient Greece (when its life was "brilliant but ineffectual"), and again for about the same period in modern Christendom. Its fruits have only begun to appear, the lands it is discovering have not yet been circumnavigated and there is no

45

telling what its ultimate influence will be on human practice and feeling. . . .

Here, indeed, is part of the essence of our paradox. Herein lies part of the reason for our symposium.

Historic Relation of Society to Scholarship

The scientist able and willing to do basic research knows his part in the microcosmos, in the company of scholars. The intellectual satisfactions and personal rewards that he can acquire by following the traditional course of his own interest and aptitude appeal strongly to the studious temperament. Indeed, they can even help greatly in living what is nowadays called the full life. Professor P. W. Bridgman in discussing "Some of the Broader Implications of Science" pointed out how personal is the issue of ideology for the scientist. (Although I feel that lately the scientist has tended to become regarded publicly as part of a large impersonal resource, as a product on which the trademark "Made in USSR" is appearing surprisingly often, along with the expected labels "Made in USA," "Made in Europe," etc.) In this connection Professor Bridgman says:

> The fundamental ideological problem which confronts us all, scientists and non-scientists alike, is the problem of finding intellectually satisfactory methods of dealing with the world around us. This problem we have always had with us. The traditional methods of attack on this problem in the past have not involved the scientist in any considerable extent, but have been rather the concern of the philosopher.

In view of the situation, what claim does society have on the basic researcher, who usually has earned his keep by teaching? As Santayana pointed out, basic research in science so far has been of little interest to mankind. Also, the scientist in his own affairs has been able to deal satisfactorily with some of the most pressing problems of personal philosophy and personal satisfaction. Why should those devoted to basic research feel that they should even consider associating their work with enterprises devoted to specific useful, social, and economic ends?

There are many immediate responses to such a query. They appear in the newspapers every day, purporting to show, for example, the responsibility of basic scientific research in relieving suffering by the conquest of diesase. But what about the suffering caused by overpopulation of the earth and the indiscriminate prolonging of the life span in an organism apparently ill-designed to integrate full faculties much beyond a few score years of life? Too, basic scientific research is exhorted to provide for the national security by the creation of more "perfect" weapons. But what about the failure of strong weapons to keep the peace in ages past and the dreadful suffering that the warring of man has caused right up to now? One of the more touching of these endless expressions of what the basic scientific researcher could do for the benefit of mankind, if he would only try, appeared in a statement a few months ago by the head of one of the important industrial associations in America. It was to provide "transoceanic television beamed from the earth and relayed across the sea from an *anchored* space satellite." Should even the heroic challenge of anchoring a space satellite be enough to make the scientist capable of basic research accept at face value the great needs that civilization says it has for him? I should think that fundamentally he could look for something more.

Prospective Relations of the
Scientist to Society

An important issue for our subject here is that he may very well find more. He may find it in a basic spiritual and intellectual coupling of scientific research with our highest human values. A few scientists, including some at this meeting, have

47

the courage to struggle with this side of the problem.* I think particularly of an essay on "The Value of Science" by Professor Richard Feynman, presented at a meeting of the National Academy of Sciences in 1956. Two particular points in Professor Feynman's paper bear very closely on deep and abiding reasons why the scientist nowadays should determine to live with the paradox of choice. First, speaking of the experience of science, he says:

> We have found it of paramount importance that in order to progress we must recognize the ignorance and leave room for doubt. Scientific knowledge is a body of statements of varying degrees of certainty—some most unsure, some nearly sure, none *absolutely* certain.

This is an utterly revolutionary, radical notion about science compared with the attitude of the general public. I believe that nowadays grave errors in understanding, ranging from the promise of cures for cancer and the effectiveness of antibiotics to the most serious aspects of national defense policy, are caused by the idea that scientific findings and judgments are absolute.

The second point related to Professor Feynman's discussion develops further the deep, pervading opportunity for scientific thought and experience really to advance the humanity of man. This is surely a call which the scientist will never ignore, when the paradox of choice of exploring science for its own sake versus following it for a particular practical end result is expressed in such terms as these. The essence of this second point of Professor Feynman is the classic truism that science teaches us how little we know and how much there is

* This matter has been eloquently reviewed by Dr. Paul Weiss in his paper, "The Message of Science," Rockefeller Institute Press, New York, 1958.

to be learned. Here lies much of the method of living with our paradox. Does Detroit know this about making automobiles, or the railroads about providing transportation, or the tobacco manufacturers about safeguarding use of their product? Recognition of this by the institutions and people who are organized for the direction and application of science and engineering would provide a powerful capacity. This capacity is for making conditions in which the gifted individual researcher feels few constraints and, in fact, is subject to no appreciable repressions in the pursuit of his studies. Yet these studies can be closely correlated with the needs, objectives, and practices of government, industry, and the public welfare! The industrial and government executive will say: "But how is the pay-off obtained? How does this fine research actually get into the product or the service needed?" From this point on we shall assume that a carefully graded development and engineering facility must be associated with all basic research whose use is desired. Careful systems engineering will first extend to development planning some appreciation of the indispensable theoretical concepts. Then, development scientists and engineers must have training and interests so broad as to cover what research uncovers.

Enlisting Basic Research
in Pursuing Goals

We shall now attempt to explain and to illustrate how this can come about. It is just by constantly renewed links between the open-mindedness and open-endedness of scientific experience and the practical needs of our society.

If this seems obvious or trite, we should recall that this is what we *don't* do now. We distrust large enterprises that seem unplanned. Yet, Dr. Warren Weaver said in a recent paper on "The Encouragement of Science":

49

> . . . what keeps the total scientific effort from being chaotic and meaningless is not central planning or any attempt to achieve it, but a kind of grand intellectual homeostasis, under which a multitude of influences interact in a natural way.

He goes on to relate this to our present position:

> Plainly our society has not yet evolved a satisfactory way of fostering creative scholarship.

But for emphasis we should refer once more to Professor Feynman's thesis. He says:

> We are at the very beginning of time for the human race. It is not unreasonable that we grapple with problems. There are tens of thousands of years in the future. . . . It is our responsibility to leave the men of the future a free hand. In the impetuous youth of humanity we can make grave errors that can stunt our growth for a long time. This we will do if we say we have the answers now . . . and thus doom man for a long time to the chains of authority, confined to the limits of our present imagination. . . . It is our responsibility as scientists, knowing the great progress and great value of a satisfactory philosophy of ignorance, the great progress that is the fruit of freedom of thought, to proclaim the value of this freedom, to teach how doubt is not to be feared but welcomed and discussed, and to demand this freedom as our duty to all coming generations.

I hope that no one will be surprised to hear that a philosophy of ignorance is the way to live with a paradox. A proper understanding by planners, leaders, voters, and thinkers of the limits of knowledge and of the uncertainty of it can make the definitions of goals and of the specific aims of industry, government, and the public welfare acceptable to the intellectual satisfactions of the basic research scientist. Thereby, highly directed elements of our society like business, the military, and public health agencies can easily include highly undirected researchers. Physical science has developed in comparatively recent times, as foreshadowed by Newtonian mechanics and introduced by the electromagnetic theory of Maxwell, a particularly elegant technique for formulating ignorance. This is generally called physical theory. It was first mostly mathematical physics, currently much theoretical physics, and probably is soon to include theoretical chemistry and theoretical biophysics.

Physical theory shows a precise, self-consistent relationship among so-called facts and also among expected observations in nature. Its ability to "handle" the endless facts of nature was dramatized by the quantum theorist Hartree. He pointed out that a book having 100 tabulations for the coordinates of each electron in an atom like argon, to give the exact wave function of A, would use up, in a single copy, all the matter in the universe. Sir J. J. Thomson succinctly made the point we are after here, when in referring to theoretical physics, he said: "A theory is a policy rather than a creed." It appears that if the extraordinary power and increasing span of physical theory and the accompanying philosophy of ignorance are allowed to play a large part in shaping our human economic and national scientific objectives, the paradox between the way of the individual scientist and the organization of science will be resolved. (That in fact such a resolution would extend much beyond great benefits to purely scientific results I have tried to show in a talk at the opening of the Cleveland Engineering and Scientific Center on "Conversion of Science to Engineering.")

Curiously enough, defects of much modern scientific organization which are often caused by narrowness and empiricism in the treatment of subject matter, are analogous to defects often attributed to our economic and political affairs. Henry A. Kissinger, in a recent article in the *Reporter*, has expressed this situation by saying:

> The deepest cause of the inhumanity of our time is probably the pedantic application of administrative norms. Its symbol may well be the "commissar," the ideal type of bureaucrat, who condemns thousands without love and without hatred simply in pursuance of an abstract duty.

This is all too reminiscent of Professor Feynman's fear that we shall settle wrongly the affairs of man for ages to come by absolutisms of today. In this same essay, Kissinger says other things in his context about policy-making which are nevertheless relevant to our central issue of directivity and pattern-making in basic research. He points out:

> The executive's task is conceived as choosing among administrative proposals in the formulation of which he has no part and with the substance of which he is often unfamiliar. . . . In our society the policy maker is dependent to an increasing extent on his subordinate's conception of the essential elements of a problem. . . . Pragmatism, at least in its generally accepted forms, produces a tendency to identify a policy issue with the search for empirical data.

Aren't some of these sharp comments on social organization and leadership pertinent to the conditions under which the basic research scientist may have to live with the paradox of choice? You can decide this, but our present point is that a unifying and predictive theory used in erecting patterns for the conduct of both basic scientific research and directed research will forcefully strengthen features highly desirable to the individual scientist and scholar.

Role of Theory in Organizing Applied Science

The ways in which knowledge of physical theory affect the organization of science in government and industry are curious and subtle. A number of diverse examples will perhaps show what is meant and at the same time give some confidence in the remarkable results obtained when a mission is formulated with the help of a general scientific theory.

Physical theory shows the possibilities of real situations, and particularly those which have not yet been realized. It liberalizes the conduct of "directed" research by indicating with the highest rationale and mental discipline that there is just not necessarily one way to do something or one way to achieve an essential or very desirable objective. This is the principle that everywhere needs to be displayed in order to couple the talents of the gifted research individualist with the needs and aims of technology. The industrial technical leader who insists that his research laboratory must turn out a better conjugated unsaturated ester for paint drying and film formation will be surprised to see that new paints such as the acrylic families involve neither unsaturation nor "drying" in the usual sense. This, you may hasten to say, is too close to technology in the first place, but it need not be if the principles of adhesion and of film formation are truly heeded even in so theatrically homely an example as the paint industry. (We'll get to some loftier examples soon, but the striking thing in this one is that there *is* beginning to be some general theory.) Then the interests of truly basic research on polymerization, on polymer film properties, on rheology, and the physics of surfaces will be available to that industry.

Similarly, in the government and in the universities the strategy of research continuing right through to development and engineering technology is then too often enslaved by a misconceived devotion to cause and effect. The freewheeling individual researcher knows that he cannot trace in advance step by step the measures necessary to invade a problem. It is a foolish conceit for an industrial laboratory or a government program, and, particularly, in military affairs for a technical fallacy known as a set of requirements, to believe that step-by-step charting of a course into the unknown can be done. Here the general philosophy so expertly advanced by Professor John von Neumann a few years ago again shows us what an insight can be gained from appreciation of theory. This is by involving what he called teleological research, and illustrated particularly by alternate concepts of classical mechanics. Thus instead of defining a state by every single step, by every single velocity of every single part at every moment, one thinks of defining its actual history by minimizing the integral of energy times time. There is bold import for much modern research in such alternatives. Research in the social sciences, in psychology, and in the life sciences could be wisely modulated by appreciation of such teleological theory.

Conditions for Depending on Guidance by Theory

So far we have said that the existence of even a crude and preliminary physical theory and the heeding of it in the expectations and patterns of operation of scientific work would permit coupling of the individual, uncommitted, undirected researcher to the general objectives of economic and social programs. There is much clear convincing evidence that the situation is about as simple as this. In the still regrettably small list of findings from basic scientific research which have been quickly and directly connected with large advances in technology and useful operations are several important examples. In these, the really new idea came out because a unifying theory had displayed the true possibilities—the wide range of means rather than simply the ends themselves. These theoretical frameworks, some of which will be illustrated, are by no means perfect and, in fact, are poorly applied when used to eliminate completely and negatively certain possibilities. It is from these misapplications that theory in science has sometimes got a bad name. Thus Professor Weisskopf, in referring to the position of atomic theory by saying: "If you understand hydrogen, you understand everything that is understood," makes a good contribution to a true philosophy of ignorance. He makes it plain that only in such cases can theories be expected to rule out possibilities. However, in a multitude of other cases they can be counted on to rule in new ideas.

In the physics of solids no one yet understands anything quite completely. Nevertheless it was the theories of Wilson, and later those of Shockley and Bardeen which led toward the finding of transistor action. This was so no matter how many government and industrial institutions wanted however desperately to fortify the coming age of electronics by facilities beyond the vacuum tube. No one had been led to examine before what the behavior of electric charges traveling at about one thousandth the speed of light would be in a crystal medium in which they could move for about 1000 atom distances before being diverted to some other direction. The theoretical possibilities of such a medium, and not the finding of a material which would yield transistors, led to interactions by Bardeen, Brattain, and Shockley with others. One was Pfann, who was aware of different sets of theories about how to achieve perfection and ultimate purity in crystals of matter. The outcome of this is an already established chapter in the history of science, involving the new process of zone refining. Even the traditional view of the pure scientist that so important a practical finding as the transistor can be a Frankenstein and devour or destroy the very freedom of inquiry which led to its creation is unfounded in the continuing research effects of zone melting. For still other theories next stood out; those of the perfection possible in crystals as proposed by Bragg and Burgers decades ago, and more recently by Read. His theoretical monograph on

(a)

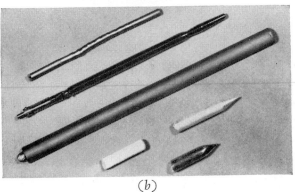

(b)

FIGURE 1. (a) Zone refining technique, discovered by W. G. Pfann, who is adjusting apparatus. By melting a little cross-sectional volume of a rod, or even hollow cylinder, and moving the molten "zone" along the length, many substances are exquisitely purified and, also, made into highly perfect, large single crystals. (b) Single crystals of elements purified by zone melting. From top of figure downward: molybdenum, silicon, germanium, aluminum, silver, and zinc.

dislocations was finished just before nearly perfect, pure crystals of germanium, prepared by zone refining, revealed crystal dislocations, at last.

(a)

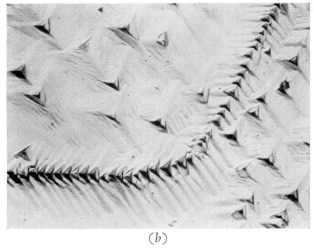

(b)

FIGURE 2. Arrays of dislocations shown by etch pits in large, pure single crystals of (a) a mineral, apatite (900×), and (b) pure antimony (665×). These reveal certain regions in the lattice where there are no atoms. This appears to be one of the most important studies of our times. It accounts for many properties of metals and also for how liquids can form into crystals.

57

Thus these theories provide a kind of continuum for the advance of science, so utterly different from the situation implied by the current term "breakthrough." That term is both blasphemy and barbarism applied to science, for the continuum is the important quality in the nurturing of basic research and in living with the paradox of choice.

Another powerful way to harmonize the freedom of the individual scholar in science with the achievement of useful and desired products is to be sure that everybody speaks the same language. This is a simple convenience which is often overlooked. It means that basic expressions of scientific concepts ought to contain common units and, hopefully, common meanings. Again, unifying physical theories, which early helped to define parameters in basic terms, are of great importance. For instance, nearly everyone would agree that a system of "electronics" has been the most vital feature of growth in chemical science and understanding in the past century. One of the first successes in identifying the versatility of bonding in carbon compounds was Kekule's concept of aromatic or benzenoid hydrocarbons. This appeared in 1866. For nearly ninety years after that, elaborate extensions of his concept accepted electrons as synonymous with electric charges. The ingenious modern notions of resonance, by Pauling, and mesomerism, by Ingold and co-workers, were linked in most minds with the distribution of the old-time electrons. Only now is arising clear realization of the relative functions of positive and negative *distributions* of charge. Largely brought out by the semi-conductor theories referred to above, we see that such charge distributions may govern the structures and reactions of vast classes of chemical compounds, but are not properly represented dynamically by the circulation of electrons. The circulation of positive and negative charges, with proper wave mechanics and with the positive holes playing a prominent role, is much more illuminating. It has recently been possible to construct thermocouples from organic solids so that at least in certain "fused ring" aromatic systems the predominant circulating charge carrier has

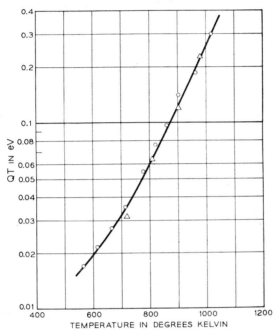

FIGURE 3. Curve showing electrical effect (voltage) from heat differences in an organic semiconductor derived from benzene-like molecules. The curve indicates that positive "holes" are predominant in charge movements.

been identified. It turns out to be *positive* in sign. A few thousand of those migrating electrons which must have plagued typesetters in the chemical formulas of hundreds of thousands of published works in the past century may be retired.

A further example of the superb results of continuity and common meaning afforded even the most complex aspects of physical science by physical theory appears in a matter involving another of the most fundamental concepts of the physical and life sciences. This is molecular weight. In the past half century, accurate methods for determination of molecular weight over a wide range of levels were based largely on such schemes as vapor density, and colligative property of solutions. Very large particles could not be handled by these techniques, even though they were the systems of greatest importance in understanding natural processes and characterizing the substance of life. Sedimentation schemes such as in the ultracentrifuge were shown to be appropriate for these large molecule systems, but there were and are many unknown properties which complicate the interpretation of sedimentation theory.

Despite the erupting interest in this century in the molecules of proteins, of carbohydrates, of cellular constituents, and of synthetic polymers (plastics, fibers, rubbers) and the great importance of measuring their size, there was essentially no new method proposed until 1943. In that year, Professor Peter Debye became interested in a problem of synthetic polymer molecular weight and remembered that his old friend, Professor Albert Einstein, had in 1910 published a paper on light scattering by liquids. In the most imaginative and theoretical terms, Professor Einstein had shown how the thermal fluctuations in the density and, hence, refraction of a liquid could be in equilibrium through osmotic tendencies. These would either average out the properties of a pure liquid through its volume or, in the case of a solution, would tend to homogenize the concentration. Now this theoretical beginning of Einstein's was continued by Debye so that he has provided a new scientific agency for the study of high molecular weights. Much of the important new work on proteins, nucleic acid complexes and synthetic polymers is immensely aided by this theory and facility.

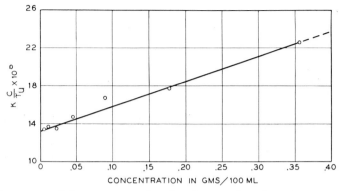

FIGURE 4. Measurement of molecular weight of synthetic glob-
ular macromolecule (polybutadiene microgel) by Debye relation.
The effect becomes larger the larger the molecule, and here a
value of 18.5 million was established.

The significant point is, however, that during the decades
between the first consideration of Einstein of the remarkable
light scattering properties of fluids and the formulation of a
relatively finished theory by Debye, hundreds of men in
scores of places worked hard on trying to adapt existing empirical methods to molecular weight determinations. The industrial and other laboratories which struggled with this problem had not succeeded in arousing genius like Debye's. Thus
experience accumulates on how basic research can, when the
proper situations are provided, influence immediately and
dramatically the course of applied science and the related
technology. And the thrift in achieving economic and social
gains resulting from providing such favorable research situations is remarkable. The conservation of resources and of materials achieved by operating on ideas instead of on empirical
and impulsive trials of hardware and (in the case of public
health), of human specimens, is huge. For contrast, Professor
T. C. Williams of Manchester noted recently:

61

. . . The raw material consumed in having an idea is negligible; the incremental fuel cost of intense mental effort has been estimated as one peanut per hour.

Influence of Physical Theory in Life Sciences

Still another aspect of these matters of resolving the paradox of choice concerns the life sciences. Here the possibility of invoking a unifying physical theory in order to guide the organization of programs and thus also to invoke the assistance of the talented individual is almost impossible at present. While brilliant hypotheses and shrewd applications of statistics have dramatically advanced our understanding of biological events and effects, there is yet hardly a case where a guiding theoretical precept is established. Further, the need is intense, because in the life sciences the fragmented structure of many gifted individuals working independently may be a problem in our present national position in science. This seems to be particularly true in medical research. Ironically, the financial support of research, particularly of basic research, in medical science is probably as easy to find now as in any other field of science. This is mostly because the issues here, that is the end needs, seem especially clear to everyone, including the Congress. Appropriations in this field approach the capacity of present qualified research laboratories to use the support. Thankfully, mostly because of the skills in the National Institutes of Health, standards are nevertheless being maintained. The shortage of individual talent in this field is presumably not because of the number of college graduates in biology (14,408 in 1958). This number slightly exceeds annually the total number of graduates in all the physical sciences (14,352 in 1958). Perhaps the choice of research in programs advancing medical science is unappealing—possibly because little unity of concept has yet appeared.

Choice for Work in Genetics

But here some favorable signs are already appearing. The realization is growing that in so complex a system as living matter there must be some special communication and control facility. Also, a further sort of recognition that Professor von Neumann's teleological research is particularly appropriate in this field has led to exciting and stimulating connections between information theory and the structure and reproducing capacity of living matter. Claude Shannon's dramatic formulation of the information content of events and the related concepts of the control of events by Professor Norbert Wiener provided general theories going far beyond the ingenious but specific treatments of signal theory and coding produced earlier. Perhaps once more it was this very quality of a unifying theory which attracted many scholars remote from communications science. As diverse but individualistic interests as represented by an astrophysicist (Gamow) and other mathematical and physical scientists have begun to show how subtle sequences of amino acids, which apparently endow protein with their high individualities and specialized functions, could be arranged by synthesis contraposed to ribonucleic acid chains. It is now believed that three or more like nucleotide residues can fix by an understandable coding scheme the position of each particular amino acid selected for the sequence desired. The protein then produced from such sequential combination would presumably be the characteristic protein for the special function, which on a higher level, of course, might also be the special function of reproduction of the whole organism itself.

Thus smoothly and quickly have some of the deepest theories of this present time moved from telephony and communications interests to genetics and familial interests. With a span like this an individual wishing to work in the field according to his own bent would have to try hard to avoid contributing to the practical advancement of the total structure. And must we not seize boldly this possibility? It is that in the life sciences embodied in genetics there is emerging a foundation of theory adequate to support a vast expansion of effort, in which the gifted worker will soon be contributing to an overall national program. Only the social sciences, whose ascendancy is certain, although we don't know when, offer comparable appeal to the deepening knowledge of genetics.

Of course, according to Professor Beadle's experience there remain language as well as theory problems in genetics. He has reported the following definition as having been obtained from a student recently: "Heredity is where if your grandparents didn't have any children, you probably won't either."

I take very seriously Professor Niels Bohr's comments in an essay on "Atoms and the Human Knowledge"

> . . . "Life" is not a word that finds any application in physics. We find no reason to describe the phenomena we deal with in classical physics in terms of life, and exactly the same is true of atomic physics. Life is, in a sense, an irreducible element in biology, just as the quantum of action is now an element in physical science; and, at any rate for the quantum of action, the essential fact is that no explanation can possibly be given for it on the basis of classical physical ideas.

In the face of this, I should not like to think of scientific programs in biology and medicine and in genetics, above all, being conducted in terms of defined objectives and a step-by-step utilization of existing concepts. Rather, as has happened in physics in the last century, we must create a situation where great new bold ideas comparable to the Maxwellian electromagnetic theory of light, to the Bohr theory of the atom, to the Planck-Einstein quantum concept must be attempted.

Freedom and Responsibility
in Nuclear Research

In this matter of the relation between freedom and responsibility of the basic research scientist, the issue of most intense
public concern is that of nuclear energy and weapons. Ironically, this has left the individual scientist with the least chance
to maintain a paradox of choice. However, the climates attained
in some of the U. S. Atomic Energy Commission laboratories
have wisely and skillfully allowed wide play for individual
interest and enthusiasm. This has been hard to do because the
great machinery and resources on the one hand and the grim
and viselike grip of national security and military requirements
on the other hand restrain freedom of choice for the free-rang-
ing mind. Despite the present frustrations of nuclear theory,
one sees the unremitting devotion of brilliant theorists to out-
lining and articulating the knowledge of nuclear fission almost
from the day it was discovered. Has this been the chief reason
why a great corps of brilliant workers in experimental research,
engineering, and further theory have been attracted to and have
felt their intellectual freedom was not destroyed by the atomic
energy and weapons programs?

However, the very strength which unifying theories have
shown, even imperfect as they have been in advancing particle
physics and nuclear research, is likely to be threatened in the
future by difficulties in communication. These obstacles have
some time ago been lucidly described by Dr. Oppenheimer.
They are based on bizarrely unfamiliar concepts, too remote
from the experience of most scientists to couple in with the
knowledge and faculties they have acquired. This situation
in nuclear physics has been eloquently outlined by Professor
Gell-Mann and Professor F. Dyson, among others. We remem-

65

ber we are trying here to illustrate some difficulties which will come in looking to evolving theory to guide a research structure and purpose in this socially sensitive field of nuclear science. Yet Professor Gell-Mann, in discussing the position of nuclear field theory, refers to Soviet concerns about *negative* probabilities, when the theory is applied to some subcritical distances. Then, in improving general understanding by use of symmetry principles in describing particle systematics it is necessary to bring in *"strangeness"* numbers and other things far beyond the intuition of even most particle theorists (and that is very far indeed). Similarly, Professor Dyson quotes a comment made by Professor Bohr recently, after a seminar given by the late Wolfgang Pauli: "We are all agreed that your theory is crazy. The question which divides us is whether it is crazy enough to have a chance of being correct. My own feeling is that it is not crazy enough."

The possible emergence of theoretical frameworks too occult for effective guidance toward a general end in research

FIGURE 5. Discovery of radioastronomy was connected with new antenna concept, produced by Karl Jansky, shown here.

programs is worrisome, but it can never be as serious as when there is no theory at all. We now have some notable examples of what can happen then. One with which I am especially familiar concerns radioastronomy, founded by Karl Jansky some twenty-five years ago. The reports of his discovery have become clouded, probably because of his early, untimely, death. Many versions of them would seem to demonstrate deep hazards in the paradox of choice. This is indeed starkly asserted in a federal report on "Basic Research, a National Resource," issued in 1957, which says: "It should be pointed out that Jansky failed to obtain support for studies which at that time had no obvious applications to practical matters." The cutting phrase "no obvious applications to practical matters" is, of course, irrelevant in the case cited, but it does bring out our present central theme.

Fortunately, an authentic account on "Early History of Radio Astronomy" has recently been published by my colleague, Dr. G. C. Southworth, inventor of the waveguide. In *The Scientific Monthly* for February 1956, Dr. Southworth documents the case that Jansky found conditions encouraging to make precise, detailed, exploration *up to the limits of knowledge of how to do it at that time,* concerning the murmurings of the universe which he had heard. As techniques and understanding advanced, there were further studies by his associates sometime after Jansky's death. The real issue was that we did not have theoretical understanding of the possible sources of such signals, or of the basic physics necessary to extend the study of these effects. Thus in the atmosphere of the laboratory in which Jansky worked there was not yet available this general fabric of concept and interrelationship, that is, of physical theory, to indicate how to have significant further pursuit of radioastronomy. For instance, it was many years after Jansky's experiments that Professor Charles Townes, then a member of

67

FIGURE 6. Early microwave spectroscopy apparatus of Dr. C. C. Townes, being operated by his assistant, Mr. Ralph Merritt, at Bell Telephone Laboratories.

the same laboratory, opened up, along with workers in Cambridge, Massachusetts, and Oxford, England, the new subject of microwave spectroscopy. From the host of contributors in that field, especially from the keen combiners of theory and experiment, have come such advances as Purcell's findings of the 21-cm wavelength emission from clouds of hydrogen gas in outer space. Now, of course, everyone knows what to do in radioastronomy, to judge by the grants made for it and the worldwide attention it is receiving.

Finally, How Will the Scientist Treat This Paradox?

We have proposed that the cultivation of unifying physical theory and ultimately of biological theory and social science theory will provide adequate circumstances for the institutions and goals of society to engage the aspirations and devotions of the free-thinking individual scientist. If so, the organizers, the leaders, the justifiers of support, those who make appropriations and those who explain to share owners, ought to hear about these ways. Put in another way, on the whole it seems much more promising for man to attempt to understand the ways of science than for science to have to learn about and adjust to the infinite variety of man. But some final words had better be said about the other side of this issue, the side which was looked at at the very first of this discussion. That is, has society, has industry, has government, have universities, in so far as they are devoted to applications of science and of basic research, really justified for the scholar reasons to sustain a paradox of choice? We have argued here that on straight intellectual bases this can be so, through the medium of adjusting our practical goals, and going toward them according to the guidance of scientific theory, or even a "philosophy of ignorance." But how about living conditions outside the ivory tower, the one that Professor Panofsky (Professor E. Panofsky, for it is well to note that there are several Professor Panofskys now) says is related to the habitation of Milton's Thinker in *Il Penseroso*:

> Oh let my lamp at midnight hour
> Be seen in some high lonely tower
> Where I may oft outwatch the Bear.

I suppose that every group at some time or other feels that it is unappreciated by society at large. I suppose that every group is also accused of special pleading. I only want to point out what we can say from our knowledge of those who work in and give richly to basic scientific research. Our civilization, that of the Free World, would do well for self interest of every human being in it now and to come to put additional material as well as spiritual values on the work of thinkers. Curiously enough, it may be that force to generate this set of values, which we believe so necessary for survival, is coming from the familiar market place practices of supply and demand. This is particularly so in the case of theorists, whose work, we have said, is essential to the proper planning and conduct of broad programs leading to economic welfare and military security. The great rarity of such gifted people, already very clearly evident in our land, is stimulating salaries and other rewards to such levels as will indeed attract more of those genetically qualified to work in basic research. Only about three years ago was the first section of theoretical physics formed in American industry, to practice the way theoretical physics has worked in universities. Only a little before that were there even sections of theoretical physics in such institutions as national laboratories, which already had rather overdefined missions. (Such missions constrain the very function in which we aver theoretical physics especially excels, that is, the function of showing how you cannot do piecemeal, by preordained steps, the fulfillment of important technical programs.)

Besides the not utterly unique influence of higher salaries, it seems likely that a number of other measures would encourage our nation's best research minds to couple with national social, industrial, and security goals. For instance, there must be increasingly free and increasingly effective publication within programs nominally directed toward immediate practical results. Here, since we are talking about basic research done in such programs, matters of proprietary interest, or security, are really relatively remote. Nevertheless, absence of a conceptual insight into what the particular field really comprises has often prevented publication of large bodies of basic results. This is on the grounds that such publication would give away commercial values or military secrets. Improvement of this situation will require not only education of those who make such decisions but equally an improvement in our facilities for the publication of important results. It seems that the emphasis on the improved publication rates, volumes, and conveniences of scientific and technical papers is much too equally divided between the unimportant and important material. Valuable impetus to the progress of basic research in national programs will come from a recognition that just as everyone agrees that not all scientific papers are of equal importance when they are published, similarly, it is not equally important to publish all of them. Presumably the new science information service functions of the federal government and the Science Information Council which is advisory to that operation will need to consider how all significant results from basic research can be communicated better. This means particularly how suitable publication by those doing basic studies in large "directed" programs can be expedited. This will maintain the quality that only the searching scrutiny and criticism of scientific peers provide.

Likewise, in the Free World system there must be a broadening of recognition of property rights represented by patents. Perhaps the classic phrase "new and unexpected" deserves a different interpretation in an age in which so much invention and discovery must inevitably be associated with theoretical patterns which indicate, if not predict, promising lines of work.

Conclusion

One of the strongest forces of life, man's curiosity and the satisfaction he gets out of exercising it according to his own bent, can be coupled with the needs and ambitions of the human race. This is our thesis about the paradox of choice. Unfortunately the measures favoring such coupling are neither quick nor easy. They mean many special and difficult advances in human capacities and training. First of all there will need to

71

be a large improvement in mathematical knowledge and skills of a large section of our technical administrative population. But is it not time that we began to look at what specific skills, as well as what ideals, are needed for the advancement of civilization? Cannot a fraction of the practice that has been given over the years to the learning of physical skills, like running, jumping, and dodging, and which (except for the last) are of diminishing importance, now be given to practice on proper levels of mathematical reasoning and exercise? If done, we would not only revolutionize such things as money changing in America, but would certainly prepare that small but necessary group which will interpret, as well as the even more necessary group which will create, conceptual science to come.

Above all, one with the rare, gifted mind can do for pure science, but yet feel that he is doing also for his fellowmen. Society must say to him the lines of John Donne:

> If thou beest borne to strange sights,
> Things invisible to see,
> Ride ten thousand days and nights,
> Till age snow white haires on thee,
> Thou, when thou return'st, wilt tell me
> All strange wonders that befell thee.

Basic Research and the LIBERAL ARTS COLLEGE

LAURENCE M. GOULD
Carleton College

I INTERPRET my assignment to be concerned only with the independent liberal arts college—not with liberal arts colleges which are parts of universities.

No one would think of defining a university leaving out basic research as one of its foundation stones. Without this ingredient a university would scarcely be one even in name. On the other hand, the role of research in the liberal arts college is much less clearly defined. Indeed, research is apparently not even recognized in the majority of them. There is, of course, a so-called educational point of view which holds that research and teaching are incompatible, but I must eliminate that from our consideration immediately.

I am not suggesting that research could or should have the same status in an undergraduate liberal arts college as it does in a graduate school. A liberal arts college is not something which has not become large enough to be a university; the basic difference is not one of size. A liberal arts college is primarily a society of teachers. The emphasis should be at this point, and the major reasons for recognition and promotion should be based upon the quality of teaching. I hasten to add that for me it is axiomatic that whereas there are research scientists who may not be good teachers, I have not known a good teacher whose competence was not increased by participation in some kind of productive scholarship. I consider scholarship man's most rewarding occupation. Likewise, I believe it needs constant renewal through some kind of research activity; otherwise it dries up its own creative sources.

Research Related to Teaching

Some would make a distinction between the approach to teaching in the liberal arts college and in other kinds of institutions. There may be some basis for the assumption that a course in science which provides fine preparation for graduate schools may not provide proper appreciation of science to the average student in the general education program. This has not been my experience; yet it is an observation which was elicited from a number of people to whom I wrote in connection with the preparation of this paper.

Recently one of my fellow college presidents, Weimar Hicks of Kalamazoo, addressed questionnaires to the presidents of the following liberal arts colleges to secure information concerning the policies governing research in these institutions: Bowdoin, Carleton, DePauw, Grinnell, Kalamazoo, Middlebury, Oberlin, Redlands, Reed, Swarthmore, Wabash, and Wooster. The results are so diffuse that it is difficult to make a summary. However, the report is brief enough so I shall quote it in its entirety.

ANSWERS TO QUESTIONNAIRE

Policy Governing Research

Question I   Do you consider time devoted to research when planning the teaching loads of individual instructors?

Answers

In all cases	4
Only when research compensated by other courses	4
In no cases	6

Question II Do you permit faculty members to apply for research grants to be projected during the academic year? If so, do you always reduce the teaching load?

Answers

Permit faculty to apply for grants during year	11
Do not permit faculty to apply for grants	2
Some time allowed for research in load of all	2
Can accept compensation only in summer	2
Might reduce load if secured a grant	8
Would reduce load only if grant pays salary	3

Question III Assume Professor Alpha can arrange a grant from General Electric for research, to be conducted by himself. The work will demand one third of Alpha's time during the academic year, and the grant is $5,000 per annum. What arrangements would you make with GE and Professor Alpha?

Answers

Place Alpha on $\frac{2}{3}$ teaching schedule and $\frac{2}{3}$ salary	6
If applied research, we would not accept	1
Charge $\frac{1}{3}$ of Alpha's salary against grant and would provide from grant a summer stipend of $\frac{2}{9}$ annual salary for summer work	1
No precedent, so no answer to this question	3
Not accept such a contract	2

Question IV What arrangement do you require to cover College overhead, carrying charges, contingencies, etc.?

Answers

Expect and usually secure 25%	1
Usually 15%	7
10–30%, and not under 15%	1
Usually 10%	1
Same as government contracts	2

It is surprising that in only four instances time devoted to research is taken account of in adjusting teaching loads. It is equally surprising that six of the replies stated that under no circumstances is it considered. Eleven permit faculty members to apply for grants to be projected during the academic year; two do not. I could go on commenting on these statistics, but the conclusion is quite clear that no two colleges are following the same policies, and it further appears that few have an established consistent policy.

By way of getting a quantitative estimate of the amount of research carried out in our liberal arts colleges, I have taken my cue from Dr. Henry F. Lewis of the Institute of Paper Chemistry and assumed a direct relationship between the production of potential Ph.D.'s and research as evidenced by the amounts of money available for that purpose in the various colleges.

When the Midwest Association of Chemistry Teachers in Liberal Arts Colleges was formed in 1953, Dr. Lewis made an intensive study of the records of one hundred colleges and the extent to which their chemistry departments were being supported by foundations or other groups in a research way. He found that the averaged data warranted some kind of valid conclusion that there was a definite relationship between the factors noted above. A review five years later strongly supported Dr. Lewis' assumption.

> Almost without exception those colleges which were productive colleges were creative colleges as measured by dollars and cents. At the same time, those which were unproductive were also non-creative using the same measurement.

Influence of Liberal Arts College on Graduate Work

The number of bachelors then who go on to achieve their doctorates reflects directly the status of research in those institutions from which they come. There are, of course, a few exceptions on either side.

Women in coeducational colleges and women's colleges are not included in these observations. Since such a small percentage (probably not more than 2 per cent) of Ph.D.'s in science are women, the production of women bachelors who go on to the doctorate would hardly give a fair appraisal of the status of research in the institutions. A few women's colleges are far superior in the production of promising scholars. The lively interest in research in three of them (Bryn Mawr, Mt. Holyoke, and Wellesley) is evidenced by the fact that they shelter chapters of Sigma Xi.

Publication 582 compiled by the Office of Scientific Personnel, National Academy of Sciences-Research Council, gives the number and origins of doctorates in all fields and the baccalaureate origins of doctorates for the twenty-one years from 1936 through 1956.

The list includes some 1166 institutions, of which 180 granted from one to 7195 doctorates during this twenty-one year period. Yet only some 100 really contributed much; in fact, three-fourths of the total number of doctorates were granted by thirty leading institutions.

The list further shows that ninety-five institutions (9.1 per cent of the total list) have produced 74 per cent of the bachelors who later achieved doctorates.

Of some 650 men's and coeducational colleges thirty have been highly productive. Yet, as Dr. Henry Lewis points out, when the total number of doctorates is considered, it is found that three out of four Ph.D.'s had their bachelor degrees in universities.

Publication 582 reveals the very modest record of most schools and the brilliance of a few.

I believe *Origins of American Scientists* by Knapp and Goodrich, published in 1952, has sometimes been mistakenly interpreted to show that the liberal arts colleges have played a more important role quantitatively than the facts show.

I believe *The Younger American Scholar,* a later study by Knapp and Greenbaum, covering the years of 1946–51, portrays the role of the liberal arts college in better perspective. Here is given the undergraduate origins of young American scholars who have won academic distinction in graduate school between 1946–51. The criteria for future scholarly promise were winning of: fellowship, scholarship, or prize of graduate level in open competition or attainment of Ph.D. The area of scholarly achievement was divided into three broad fields: *science, social science,* and *humanities.*

The index was computed by dividing the number of male scientists by the estimated total number of male graduates. Of the fifty leading institutions, thirty-two were liberal arts colleges, and of the twenty institutions having highest male indices in science, ten were liberal arts colleges. The twenty institutions in order of excellence were: California Institute of Technology, Swarthmore, Chicago, Reed, MIT, Augustana, Oberlin, Johns Hopkins, Antioch, Cooper Union, Carleton, Purdue, Cornell, Brooklyn, Wooster, Princeton, Berea, De-Pauw, Harvard, and Beloit. The top, Caltech, had an index of 38.2, Beloit one of 9.8.

Eight institutions appear on all three lists (*science, social science,* and *humanities*), namely, Swarthmore, Reed, Chicago, Harvard, Oberlin, Antioch, Carleton, and Princeton. Obviously, the academic climate which stimulates the production of scientists is likewise hospitable to intellectual achievement in other fields.

In collecting material for this paper, I naturally picked the minds of my own immediate colleagues as well as those of individuals I have known in other liberal arts colleges. I asked the following questions by way of getting reactions:

78

1. What is the real relationship between research and teaching?

2. Are you giving proper treatment to students who promise to have the capacities for careers in basic research?

3. What are the particular factors that make it difficult to enlarge or improve the activities of scientific creative scholarship in the liberal arts college?

4. What are some specific aspects of research in institutions like Carleton which are unparalleled elsewhere?

Naturally, my questions as indicated above were sent to people doing research; therefore, the answers are slanted, as it were. There was, of course, general agreement that basic research is an essential ingredient of the educational process whether it be in a liberal arts college or elsewhere.

I should like to quote from a response to my questions from a young colleague of my own college.

> When I came to Carleton I thought that I had made a basic decision to the effect that I was choosing a career in teaching rather than in research. With each passing year it becomes more painfully obvious how naïve this view actually was. For myself the separation of teaching and research has come to appear as a ridiculous impossibility. Were I to try to live off the fat of my Ph.D. for long, both my students and I would starve intellectually. Each year I realize more and more that my fundamental limitation as a teacher is my limitation in productive scholarship.

This, of course, is the kind of testimony that we should expect from every effective teacher whether he is in science or not.

Advantages of Research
in Liberal Arts College

There was further general agreement that research can be a much more effective teaching tool in the liberal arts colleges than it can be in undergraduate colleges of a university. In the latter the instructor's interests must be divided between

79

the undergraduate and graduate students. In the liberal arts college the instructor's concern is focused entirely on the undergraduate at a time in his development when basic decisions concerning a career must be made.

Another general reaction was that competent scholars in the liberal arts college are more apt to be able to consider problems simply because they interest them than might be true in a larger, more complex university or research institution. Even though they work in laboratories which are often small and ill-equipped, a recurring observation was that the individual has much more room to move about. A further general observation was that research in the liberal arts college was much more likely to develop along the lines of pure research, or stated differently, the avenues for pure research are much wider than those for applied research. In general, small liberal arts colleges do not have the resources to undertake applied research to any large extent. In none of the responses to my questions did I receive any comment about the place of applied research in liberal arts colleges.

Most of my informants believe that we could improve our programs to give better opportunities to students who promise to have the capacities for careers in basic research. Whereas a goodly number find it easy and desirable to carry on some modest research programs on the part of students during the academic year, the bulk of my informants believe that much more attention should be given to the utilization of young scholars in summer programs. This is easier in liberal arts colleges, which for the most part do not demand the time of their staff for summer teaching. During the coming summer (1959) at Carleton College, twenty students in biology, chemistry, and mathematics will be carrying out research projects worthy of the name, in close cooperation with members of our staff.

Here are some further more specific answers to the question as to the special advantages for research in small, liberal arts colleges.

1. The easy, informal relationships between the teacher and the potential scholar, which make it easier for the students to discover how facts are obtained, how they are used, and how an interpretation of them can lead not only to an understanding of many observed phenomena but also prepares the way for tackling new situations.

2. One very productive scholar replied that given capable staff, equipment, and support, "A small college has a tremendous advantage arising from its informality, its intimate relations between students and faculty, its relatively quiet and peaceful atmosphere, and the fact that its students are at a more impressionable age than in the graduate schools."

3. Most commented upon size in itself being a real advantage because of the stimulation it provided for interdisciplinary relationships. Departmental boundaries are apt to be less rigid, and in most institutions the sciences and mathematics are held together in a single division with a chairman. This means that papers presented are challenged by people from a variety of different fields. Such challenges and such interdisciplinary stimulation encourage research in overlapping areas.

4. Several replies called attention to the fact that a little isolation is a good thing and may be conducive to development of original ideas. "Working by oneself permits individuality," said one biologist.

5. At least one gifted teacher and scholar believes that in the best liberal arts college there is a larger possibility of recognizing and encouraging excellence. More opportunity to set a few individual students on fire at the time when the ignition of such a blaze makes all the difference in the world.

Let me now give you some of the many responses to my inquiry about the limiting factors in the development of creative scholarship in the liberal arts colleges.

1. Lack of encouragement on the part of college administration seems to be not uncommon. In some cases productive scholarship is not just frowned upon; it is actually not permitted.

2. Too many courses, too heavy teaching loads.

3. Inadequate library facilities.

4. Lack of contact with fellow scientists, lack of opportunity of rubbing elbows with people in closely related fields.

5. Lack of trained assistants.

6. Lack of equipment.

7. Lack of funds, though surprisingly and hopefully this was not placed at the top of the list in many cases. It is still a most important item, however.

8. Discrimination between the independent liberal arts college and the university. Other things being equal, the university gets preferred treatment in securing grants from foundations, corporations, etc.

By and large, it is obvious that the advantages of pure research (without regard to teaching) in a liberal arts college are heavily overweighed by the disadvantages. Our task, therefore, is to exploit and increase, so far as possible, the advantages. Of course, now and again one comes across one of those rare individuals in a small liberal arts college who can hold his own at all levels with the best of his colleagues anywhere. Here is a comment about one:

> Let me cite an example of a liberal arts biologist who has competed successfully with his university counterparts. This man taught between eighteen and twenty-five hours a week, advised about forty students, put two sons through medical school, spent every summer at a research station, worked at least five nights a week in his modest, poorly equipped laboratory, published furiously and well, retired at the age of sixty-seven, and returned to teaching because he felt lost.

Work of first-rate quality is frequently carried out at the undergraduate level. Not long ago a new determination of the atomic weight of fluorine was reported from Reed College. This work was largely that of undergraduate chemistry majors.

In 1957 the Chicago section of the American Chemical

Society sponsored a research symposium for undergraduates. Colleges and universities from the neighboring states were invited to participate, the stipulation being that the work presented must have been done by an undergraduate and must be original. The outstanding paper which won first prize was from a small, little known college.

In 1958 a similar undergraduate research symposium was sponsored by the Minnesota section of the American Chemical Society. Fourteen papers were received both from liberal arts colleges and universities. Again the first prize was won by a paper from a small college.

These symposia are important for their actual results but even more for the stimulation to the participants. One able teacher and scholar makes this comment about the symposia: "The professional polish our students have and the very high caliber of presentation of papers is something which continually astounds the industrial judges at these meetings."

I have said very little about support, for to dwell on the need for it would be to elaborate the obvious. But I think I should point out that a great many things are not gotten

Table I

Type of Gift	Rank in	
	College Preference	Corporation Practice
Unrestricted funds	1	5
Capital funds for endowment	2	8
Capital funds for buildings	3	2
Scholarship funds	4	3
Funds for new equipment	5	6
Graduate fellowship funds	6	7
Specified departmental funds	7	4
Research funds	8	1

because they are not asked for. In 1954 The Council for Financial Aid to Education asked colleges to list eight types of gifts in the order of their usefulness to the college. The same types of gifts were ranged in the current practice in corporation giving. The results are given in Table I. Note that whereas research funds held first place in corporate giving, they were given lowest priority by the colleges.

Conclusions

I should like to make the following observations by way of conclusion:

1. While support from foundations and other sources for research in liberal arts colleges has been somewhat niggardly, it appears that college administrators should take a more aggressive attitude.

2. Support on a broader basis and for longer periods of time is urgently needed. Parenthetically, while a pure research professor is not normally thought of as a member of a liberal arts college faculty, the presence of an occasional one might be an excellent catalyst.

3. More support is needed for undergraduate research, both for its own sake but even more for the role it plays in recognizing talent early and encouraging it accordingly.

4. Some kind of educational program is needed for college administrators and trustees to awaken them to a realization of the importance of basic research and to its fundamental function in the teaching process and therefore to its legitimate place in the liberal arts college.

5. More weight should be given to the recognition of research as one of the bases of promotion and increase in salary.

6. More attention should be given to the development of an academic climate which is friendly to research. For instance, Sigma Xi brings together teachers from all scientific fields with

inevitable exchange of ideas, and election to associate member-ship is a motivating factor in stimulating the youthful scientist-to-be. It is all the more surprising therefore to discover that only eight liberal arts colleges have chapters of Sigma Xi and three of these are women's colleges.

I cannot too strongly reemphasize the fact that the aca-demic climate which is hospitable to science must be no less friendly to intellectual values in other fields. No greater dis-service could be done to science than to raise the level of science education without raising the level of all education. It is a chief task of the liberal arts college to emphasize the fundamental unity of knowledge—to hold before its students the idea that the pursuit of wisdom is still basically a single enterprise.

In spite of the superior performance of the few, the total record of our liberal arts colleges in research and the training of scientists is not impressive. It is neither as good as it should or could be. But I think it is improving as more funds are being made available for research and more attention is drawn to its fundamental role in discovering scientific potentialities at the undergraduate level.

Consideration of the need for more and better scientists and the dimensions of our task, I would hazard the guess that we shall examine few areas of potential basic research in this symposium where there is greater opportunity for healthy growth than in our liberal arts colleges.

Basic Research and the STATE UNIVERSITY

C. A. ELVEHJEM
The University of Wisconsin

FEW SUBJECTS interest me more than the one assigned to me today. I have had the opportunity to carry on basic research in a state university for many years, and for some of those years I was responsible for the administration of a program helpful to research. My enthusiasm for this speaking assignment stems from those experiences.

Although I do not expect to sermonize, I have a text, taken from the *President's Review* in the 1957 Rockefeller Foundation annual report:

> Corporate members of the community of science and scholarship, the universities have served as trustees of man's intellectual inheritance and a prime source of its progressive enrichment.

This statement, I believe, gives adequate recognition to the close relationship between basic research and universities. It does not, of course, differentiate between private and state universities. This distinction, I believe, is not nearly as significant as some suggest, but I will, in accordance with my assignment, limit the major portion of my remarks to the state university.

87

Early Research

I think it is important to point out, at the start, that research did not originate in our universities. The university we know today developed largely in France and Italy at the beginning of the second half of the Middle Ages. Oxford was established in 1264, Prague in 1348, and Vienna in 1365. These universities gave little consideration to research.

In the seventeenth century there was a significant burst of scientific activity, but much of the experimentation was carried out in the homes of the experimenters rather than in university laboratories. Newton's optical researches were made in his home. Robert Boyle tested his laws of elasticity of gases in tubes along the stairway of his house.

In America during the colonial period, scientific work was carried out sporadically, but for the most part, outside the universities. Franklin and Jefferson, for example, were not attached to academic institutions.

But as the modern American university developed, research became an integral function. During the past few years, several state institutions have celebrated the seventy-fifth anniversary of their agricultural experiment stations. Thus, we can trace, for at least three quarters of a century, formalized and recognized research, at least in the colleges of agriculture, in a number of state institutions. It could be argued that these programs were not, in the beginning, much concerned with basic research; in fact, they were called experimental stations. Undoubtedly much testing and pot boiling was carried out without the development of new basic ideas.

Evidence that the significance of basic research in state universities was not widely recognized, even at the beginning of this century, is revealed in the strength of the plea for its recognition by Thomas E. Chamberlin at the Jubilee Celebration of The University of Wisconsin in 1904.

I should explain that Dr. Chamberlin had been president of The University of Wisconsin from 1887 until 1892, when he went to Chicago in order to devote his full energies to research in geology. He returned to make the Commencement address in 1904. And he spoke in these words:

> . . . the fundamental promotion of education lies in increase of the intellectual possessions of a people, and in the mental activities and attitudes that grow out of the getting, the testing, and the using of these possessions.

He continued:

> The education of the individual does not necessarily lift the education of the aggregate, for if we convey to the rising generation only such ideas as we have inherited, the summit-level of education is not raised.

He further added:

> If we are agreed upon this, let us turn to the question: How is real educational advancement to be secured?
>
> Some progress may be made in a live people by voluntary research and by the incidental accretions of common experience, but if our intellectual estate be left to such sporadic and unsystematic agencies, growth is a creature of uncertainty. If perchance there be laudable growth, it is scant credit to the state. If the enrichment of our intellectual world be left to spontaneous individual action, it cannot be hoped that it will be continuous or systematically directed. It will follow the diverse lines that chance to be inviting to individuals. Inquiries will be taken up and dropped at pleasure, and will be limited by scant resources. There is as good chance of finding a rich man in heaven as in a laboratory.

Dr. Chamberlin concluded:

> Research in every realm of a people's legitimate interest is an appropriate function of the people's organized self, the state, and of the people's organized instrument of research, the state university.

89

He closed with a plea that the University of Wisconsin become a leader in basic research:

> . . . no institution has yet fully entered upon it. . . . Which shall be the first to become predominantly an institution of research? Which shall be the first to fulfill the high destiny of an ideal state university?

I am sure that were he here today, some fifty years later, he would be astonished at the magnitude of our answer to his challenge, both at Wisconsin and on a national scale, and at the magnitude of the problems we have as a result.

During the past two decades, for example, our national research budget has increased some fifteenfold, if we take into account the changes in the value of the dollar. Today the national economy supports about a quarter million active scientists although only 10 per cent conduct basic research. The rate of growth of research in this country is probably greater than growth of any other single activity. At least four entirely new industries have been created by recent scientific advances—chemical, electronic, nuclear energy, and pharmaceutical—and application of these fields to older industries is almost universal.

From the evidence around us, it could not be more apparent that there is a strong social and economic demand for research, at least of the variety that is commonly regarded as being capable of fairly rapid transformation into tangible evidence of progress. The major part of support in this country goes into applied research and development rather than into basic science. Support is heavily slanted toward the physical sciences, and at the present time a large part of our total research activities are for military purposes.

The "industry of discovery," as Sumner Slichter terms it, is now recognized as one of our major producers of investment opportunity. Slichter points out, in fact, that the vital capacity of a modern economy to create investment possibilities depends mainly upon the fund of accumulated knowledge and the volume of research. He adds:

> Indeed, it is safe to say that there is no field where larger government expenditures would produce as rich a return as greater outlays on research—and also on the necessary foundations for research, the education of a talented people.

The Incentive

I think these reasons, plus those put in terms of human health, happiness, intellectual satisfactions, and fulfillment of our seemingly unquenchable desire to know as much as we can concerning the world around us and of our own destiny would be sufficient to justify our concern over how we can best serve the cause of research. We now have, however, another and most forceful reason. For the first time in history we are confronted with a dynamic civilization which has threatened to become the technological equal of our own. And at the present time, to use the words of Howard L. Bevis, "we have more faith in the communists to work diligently for their goal of world domination than we have in ourselves to work diligently for our goal of world brotherhood." With this as our premise, we must accept the fact that for an undetermined length of time to come we are to be in direct competition with an opposing ideology and economy for the hearts and political allegiances of men. This competition is to continue throughout a period of extreme population growth in those countries which are geographically most closely allied to our competition and which now are experiencing a political and technological awakening. We feel certain that moral right weighs most heavily on our side; there are some doubts that we will have sufficient economic or military strength to defend it.

I have heard it said that present generations of youth are stagnating because they have no cause for which to work. I think that, if this is indeed true, it is because we as educators and scientists have been somehow delinquent, or perhaps only reticent, in speaking out about the things that deep in our hearts we believe. We have been silent in the face of accusations that we are ourselves mere technicians who are training technicians to fill our shoes in the next generation. We have been accused of erecting a vast monolithic structure of science and technology whose machines are in imminent danger of running off with all of us. We have been told time and time again that even though the threat of war were eliminated, we face, as a nation, grave and nearly insurmountable problems, such problems as dwindling supplies of resources, problems of a burgeoning population, problems of supplying food enough for everyone, problems of energy sources, genetic problems, radiation problems, problems of technological unemployment and too much leisure. Personally, I cannot wholly subscribe to the view that any of the social or economic problems we will encounter as a result of scientific and technological progress will be any greater than, to take an example, the readjustment made necessary by the mechanization of farming or the development of rapid transportation. The revolutions we have already gone through are perhaps as great as any we will encounter in the course of peaceful evolution of our society.

Dr. R. A. Millikan, who died in December, 1953, at the age of 85, used to remark that he belonged to the first generation of men in the whole history of the world who have been able to say that physical conditions of living were substantially different for their children than such conditions had been for the parents. It is my personal conviction that the possibilities to which men can aspire are limitless, that we are merely at the beginning of our road rather than at the end. However, I am also convinced that some of the greatest obstacles we must hurdle to reach good ground, where steady, forthright, progress can be undertaken, will be encountered within the next few years or decades. Once beyond these, it seems to me that we will be on a plateau where the problems we shall come upon, as a species inhabiting a fairly friendly planet, will not seem much greater than those we have as a result of the development of tractors and trains. If surviving through to our plateau is not a cause worth working for, I don't know of one that is. It is for us, then, to make the challenge clear.

I have a phrase that has stuck in my mind for some years now, and I have forgotten its author, but it goes something like this:

> We who are living today are characters in a legend, an incredible, hell-shot legend, but nevertheless a legend; the greatest ever told, for either we are on the verge of damnation or the conferring upon us of divine honors. Which it shall be, only the destinies know.

At the present time, man controls his destiny, within limits, and I am convinced we are capable of controlling it even more intensively to build a better life for all mankind.

My assignment today, however, as I see it, is not to discuss man's ultimate destiny, but rather to outline some of my ideas as to how the cause of basic research can be furthered, particularly with the state universities in mind. I think we can all agree that the amount of research we now do is a small part of the amount we could do before reaching the point of diminishing returns. I think we all agree that the growth of research will be approaching exponential during the coming years, and that we must take some time to consider such practical things as where are we going to put the laboratories and how are we going to pay the people. Harold Taylor recently said that money is what college presidents talk about, while businessmen, admirals, and bankers talk about education. I have been president of the University of Wisconsin for about a year now, and I am beginning to see what he means.

Encouragement by Government Support

Without doubt, much of the money is going to have to come from the federal government. At the present time, the Department of Defense contributes some $300 million a year for research under university direction. The 1959 appropriations of the National Science Foundation provide an additional $130 million. We have a six-year federal program providing for loans to gifted students with a billion dollar price tag. We have had such agencies established as the National Aeronautics and Space Administration, apparently with some $250 million available to it for research, and we have the continuing programs in the field of atomic energy, with new ones promised in astronomy and a number of other fields. Add to this the $5 to $10 billion being spent by industry largely for research and development, plus the one or two billion provided by private foundations and state appropriations to university research, and you have some idea of the magnitude of our present scientific venture.

For the universities this means that, in addition to conducting a large amount of contract research, we must continually train good scientists to man the steadily expanding scientific program. Fortunately research and education run hand in hand —the best way to train a young scientist is to have him spend part of his time studying and the other part working directly on a research project. Thus, in universities we have available what might be termed a fairly inexpensive technical labor force. Moreover, the individuals making up this labor force have an intense interest in their subject, are eager to work long hours, and it is not possible to consider them as merely an item on the

94

cost sheet because they represent an investment in the future as well.

Universities, thus, are ideally set up to conduct a major proportion of the national research effort. In industry, it has been estimated that at least a three-to-five-year period is required before dividends from any one research project may begin to pay out. On top of this, it is reported that, while a definite study on project failure rates has yet to be done, only one project in eight is ever worth while, and this has been termed an excessive rate for many of the smaller or medium-sized industries to support. In universities, however, we take little note of the percentage of experiments that fail to turn out in the way we thought they would, and as a matter of reality often consider negative results as important from the point of view of knowledge gained as a result confirming an original hypothesis. This is because we are primarily interested in knowledge and not profit. Any knowledge acquired, in our terms, is profit in itself.

This is not to say that we can conduct all kinds of research more profitably than industry, and that industry should, therefore, turn its laboratories over to us. In a competitive world, the yields from research are fast becoming a necessity for economic survival of individual organizations and much developmental research will continue to be performed by industry, if for no other reason than the fact that the result of research will be available only to the sponsor and not dumped immediately into the hopper of knowledge from which everyone can take what he wants or needs. Furthermore, much developmental research can best be conducted by individuals whose interests are tied closely on a long-term basis to that of the organization with which they are associated. This type of arrangement creates a personal motivation which might otherwise not be particularly strong.

This eliminates from the scope of state university work

much developmental research of the type devoted to improving a particular commodity or commerce. It does not, however, eliminate either basic research or what we can term applied research, if we define the latter as the investigation of ways and means of transforming basic research findings into general practical improvements in our way of life. As I indicated earlier, it was in this particular developmental area that research had its start in state universities. All the state institutions have had a long history and have built a strong tradition of service to their respective commonwealths through the experiment stations which were set up as part of the land grant colleges. They have had long experience with the efficient administration of state and federal research funds, and they possess dedicated research staffs composed of many outstanding individuals who have amply demonstrated through the years both scientific competence and a certain devotion to the broader ideals of mankind through the acceptance of rewards which have been largely intellectual. I am determined not to mention the word salary.

I realize that in saying these things I am running directly against an idea current in industrial research that conditions there are more pleasant than they are in universities. Conditions in these two places are different, I will agree, and I see no need to expand this point. But I feel that it is not true that industry is consistently providing better research facilities, more stimulating problems, more efficient administration, and working conditions more congenial because the scientist is unhampered by a repetitious teaching load and the need to construct certain items of equipment himself. Some people find greater stimulation in applied problems than basic ones. Some people like to teach. I think the world of research is sufficiently large to accommodate them all. Our problem at the present time is to get as many people as we can into their proper places, for we lose a great deal in terms of initiative if we do not.

Freedom and Research

The matter of freedom is also one that looms large in the eyes of many of our scientists, and by freedom I mean two kinds of freedom, freedom to investigate and freedom to publish. Both, of course, will always be restricted in a competitive enterprise, and for this reason universities will always attract the kind of people who are interested more in fundamentals than applications. While I am discussing the matter of freedom, I would also like to worry the old bone comfortably named disparity in freedom between state and privately endowed institutions. There is, in my own experience, extremely little curtailment of freedom in the state universities, and I often wonder if the entire issue is not meaningless. Both state and privately endowed universities are organized and administered along the same general lines and according to the same general rules. Both are governed by a board of individuals, named regents, trustees, or governors, who in all essential respects are greatly similar. The schools are staffed by faculty members who are reasonably zealous and admirably articulate when defending the issues of academic freedom. In fact, we at Wisconsin have a history of which we are particularly proud. At the close of one particular chapter in the defense of academic freedom at Wisconsin, the details of which would not interest you now, the regents asked to have these words set in bronze and affixed to the entrance of our Bascom Hall:

> Whatever may be the limitations which trammel inquiry elsewhere, we believe that the great State University of Wisconsin should ever encourage that continual and fearless sifting and winnowing by which alone the truth can be found.

We have taken strength and renewed determination from this plaque more than once since it was cast in 1910, and it has served well on many occasions as an affirmation of the

97

tradition of academic freedom at Wisconsin, a tradition which, because of our history and because of the plaque, is well known to nearly everyone, difficult to attack, and not too difficult to defend. There are possibly private institutions which are at a greater disadvantage than we when the issues of academic freedom arise and our right to pursue the truth as we see it is in danger of infringement.

But to return to my major thesis, these are all reasons for my conviction that the greatest expansion of facilities and personnel for the nation's basic and applied research programs should come within our university research framework. This is not to say that I believe these two fields of endeavor should be the exclusive property of universities. I fully expect that a large portion of these forms of research, particularly applied research, will continue to be conducted by the larger industries and by the foresighted and ambitious smaller industries. In many highly specialized fields it may even be most efficient to have industry conduct government contract research. In many instances, industry must conduct a certain amount of basic research to solve some immediate problems in applied research, or even to satisfy the innate curiosity of investigators who work primarily on applications but have an urge to conduct research on some phenomenon which has aroused their special interest. I am aware that some of our most important basic work has been done by individuals under just these conditions, but by and large I believe that the opportunities for greater freedom of investigation provided by a university atmosphere will, in the long run, be more productive of the kind of basic knowledge which finds application in many different fields. As an example of basic research with broad possibilities of application, let me point out that it was a basic investigation of the cause of a disease of cattle which led to the discovery of dicumarol in our agricultural laboratories at Wisconsin, and dicumarol, as many of you know, is now used widely in human medicine. It is particularly interesting to me—because it has involved a good share of my scientific career—that the antipellagra factor, niacin, was isolated by a group of workers, myself included, who had never seen a human patient with the disease. I think this story will also illustrate some other points I would like to make.

It was well established in the medical records that in the nineteenth century some 5 per cent of the population in certain countries died each year of pellagra. The first case was observed in this country in 1863, and by 1912 we had 30,000 cases with 40 per cent fatality. At first it was believed that pellagra was an infectious disease. Then Dr. Joseph Goldberger demonstrated to his own satisfaction, at least, that it was a disease caused by nutritional inadequacy. These facts, however, would not have seemed particularly pertinent to us in 1930 when we were working to prepare a highly purified ration to feed animals, one with which we could produce specific deficiencies by leaving out one or another of the nutrients.

When a natural ration was heated under moist conditions, and fed to chicks, we obtained the typical dermatitis of pellagra, known for many years in human beings and observed by a number of workers in dogs. This was the first time that the effect had been observed in so convenient a laboratory animal as the chick, however, and we decided then and there that we were on a particularly promising lead and that an important problem would be the isolation of the antipellagra factor, with the chick used as the experimental animal.

Our plans were interrupted when I was granted a fellowship and a leave of absence to study in England, and this in itself is representative of the attitude of most administrations toward scientists involved in basic research—it is important that the individual be given every opportunity to broaden his knowledge in those fields which he feels are important to the exploration of his particular problem. In England I worked on the possible relationship of vitamins to enzymes and during this time I had the good fortune to meet a visiting Indian student who was working on the B complex. He borrowed some liver extract which I had taken with me from Wisconsin and after working on it for a few days found, to his excitement, that it was an extremely rich source. When I returned to Wisconsin some months later I was confident that in liver we had a supply of the antipellagra factor if only we could strain it out. Seven years later, after many disappointments, we had the material crystallized. It seemed to resemble a coenzyme that Otto Warburg had characterized earlier, and when we fed these substances to different groups of animals the result was identical. Within a few weeks Dr. Tom Spies was using nicotinic acid, now niacin, as an agent in the treatment of pellagra.

This story of niacin, which I took because I had some first-hand knowledge of its discovery, is typical of many hundreds of histories of basic research developments. Had I not been permitted a year's work in England we might very well have gone way off the track in our work. And only in a university would I have been permitted seven years of what, to a balance sheet, would have been totally profitless effort. The work virtually eliminated pellagra as a serious public health threat, but probably equally important from the standpoint of scientific knowledge, we were learning things of value about enzymes and vitamins all along the way in our seven-year search. The fact that we were finally successful was gratifying, but our work would have been significant if we had failed our final goal. There were, in fact, six other teams of researchers close behind us, and I am sure one of them would have hit upon nicotinic acid if we had not. And all contributed valuable additions to our fund of fundamental knowledge concerning vitamins and nutrition.

The Isolated Researcher

I think this is also a good example to illustrate another point that I would like to make, and one that is probably abundantly obvious to all by this time. We still have examples of invaluable contributions made to mankind's knowledge by isolated workers with an urge to stretch beyond the confines of a narrow task. But by and large, we must recognize that the bread-and-water diet is no longer sufficient to foster the kind of scientific development we most urgently need. Research has become one of our social and economic institutions, and we must exercise a certain amount of caution to see that it is organized most efficiently for all concerned, for the individuals who conduct research and for society as a whole.

By efficiency I do not necessarily mean the kind of efficiency that comes under the category of cost accounting, and perhaps here I may be treading on dangerous territory. But creative scientists are more closely allied to creative artists than we might ordinarily think, and while, like artists, they are with rare exceptions willing and eager to stay within an established budgetary figure, they are not able to do their proper work and keep track of where every penny goes at the same time. I know that this is necessary in industry and perhaps even in government and to some extent in universities, but I firmly believe that basic scientific research is not compatible with the modern refinements of cost accounting. The human mind is incapable of thinking of more than two or three things at a time, and it can concentrate on only one with any degree of intensity. To ask a scientist working on the intricacies of nuclear physics to be, in addition, a bookkeeper, is asking too much.

This is one reason universities require overhead allowances for each project, allowances which are intended to help maintain the building in which the research is to be conducted and pay for the electric lights, heat, and the accounting personnel and machines needed to keep the record straight. In the past, universities have been in large measure content with what has actually been an unreal overhead figure because they considered it part of their educational function to conduct research, and the difference between overhead received and overhead required was budgeted as an educational cost. As we expand our laboratories, however, to perform our social obligations as research institutions, it is only realistic that we must also ask for a more accurate appraisal of what our overhead actually will be and that all identifiable indirect costs be recognized.

Although the amount of money for research in universities steadily increases, the grants are still provided on a project basis, with no provision made for building new laboratories and equipping these laboratories with modern apparatus. This places universities at something of a disadvantage because in most instances we must, with rising enrollments, place first priority on classroom and dormitory space. It is conceivable that, unless provision for laboratory construction is included in many of our project contracts, we may find in a relatively short time a sudden shift in the amount of basic research from universities to industry despite the obvious advantages universities possess for this type of research. This is especially true in the field of engineering, and to some extent in medicine, where very expensive equipment is required. I do not mean to imply that this is going to take place; I believe we have sufficient foresight to avert any significant trend in this direction, but it would be appropriate to devote some thought and planning to the expansion of university scientific facilities at this stage in our development.

It has also been pointed out that the alternative to direct federal financing of laboratory construction on our campuses would be the adoption of policies which would provide schools with incentives to finance such facilities on their own. The suggestions made at a National Research Council meeting included allowances for more rapid amortization and depreciation of university-financed facilities. However, it seems to me that it is also imperative that when a large project is undertaken, one requiring construction of additional buildings and the acquisition of expensive equipment, we be assured of continuing support. This is particularly important to us now in engineering and medicine. In both of these fields I believe we can anticipate particularly rapid expansion in the near future. The high costs of the laboratories and equipment needed for the expanding research programs in these particular areas are inclined to render universities somewhat cautious about undertaking projects on a short-term basis, with the possibility that future maintenance will have to be deducted from the funds now obtained from non-federal sources and devoted largely to instruction in the humanities and social sciences, arts and letters.

There is one more aspect of this rapid expansion based on contract which I think could be improved. I believe it is unfair to ask some of our finest scientific investigators to be continually on the alert for a place to land when their contracts expire. As our programs expand, more and more of our scientific personnel will fall into the non-tenure category, and we will be at a severe competitive disadvantage in securing staff members of the quality we will need. To meet this particular problem we may find it necessary to expand greatly our practice of establishing research professorships so that outstanding research scientists can be attracted to universities to work without

formal teaching responsibilities other than to assist in the training of graduate students. I think everyone agrees that this is an
ideal method of insuring substantial returns for each research
dollar spent, and I believe we must take steps to have the practice more generally adopted.

Only by fulfilling our responsibilities as research institutions can we expect to meet our obligations as teaching institutions as well. As I pointed out earlier, on the level of graduate
education we can teach the methods and aims of active research
only by requiring each student to participate in one of our
research projects. The value of research to teaching operates
on the undergraduate level as well, for only by having a large
number of faculty members who are active researchers can we
expect to produce bachelor degree candidates who are fully
aware of contemporary progress, not to mention promises and
potentialities, in their respective fields of specialization.

It is important that state universities continue to maintain
their position as research institutions, for in numerical terms
they consistently educate the largest number of advanced
students, and only by maintaining our research efforts can we
hope to continue to produce the numbers of skilled scientists
which will be required by our future economic, educational,
and defense efforts.

It was recently revealed that during the period 1956-57,
land-grant colleges and state universities conferred 53 per cent
of all doctorate degrees, 69 per cent of doctorates in the biological fields, 64 per cent in engineering, 71 per cent in the health
professions, 59 per cent in the physical sciences. As enrollments
increase generally, I doubt that these percentages will change
appreciably and the burden for educating the research men,
the university teachers, and leaders in industrial technology,
will fall to the land-grant schools and to the private institutions in the same proportions it has in the past. If it is an intel-

lectual challenge that this nation faces, our success in meeting it will be determined by our success in producing great intellectual leaders.

In summary, then, I believe the state universities can contribute much toward the successful furtherance of our national scientific effort, particularly in the areas we designate as basic research; but that as we expand in these fields, we must be assured of the kind of financing which will permit us to build our program on a long-term basis and which will help us solve more problems than we create. It will also help us in our efforts to broaden the educational experiences which we attempt to provide. Some of our sharpest growing pains will come from the fact that great numbers of our people do not understand the place of science in our lives, and I am now speaking both of the physical world of medicines and machines and of the intellectual world of values and philosophies. It is the role of education to help all men learn to live in our world, to have an appreciation for its values, its varied cultures, economics, and political traditions. We must work out our educational and research programs, and our national life, so as to serve all our needs and ideals and not permit some to be furthered at the cost of others, but it should be apparent to all by now that scientific endeavor has attained a dominant position in our society and that it is essential that we begin to formulate broad policies for its continued expansion.

Basic Research
and the PRIVATE
UNIVERSITY

LEE A. DuBRIDGE
California Institute of Technology

I WISH to introduce this subject by talking about research problems at *one* private institution—Caltech. I know that these problems will be found in other institutions, both private and public. And I know also that quite different problems may be found by still other institutions, both private and public.

Caltech is a small private institution with a highly selected student body, restricted to about 700 undergraduate and 500 graduate students. When it was reorganized into its present form in 1920, it became devoted to the proposition that research and teaching should be inseparable activities in a school of science and engineering. Hence small teaching loads, adequate funds for research, and a small student body selected for its creative and research potential have always been the ideals, and these ideals have, to a substantial extent, been achieved.

A second pair of ideals was also adopted, namely, that all research activities should be of a basic nature aimed at the extension of knowledge, but, at the same time, the Institute would choose its fields of interest in such a way as to be of

107

maximum service to the community and to the nation. Thus, at the same time that cosmic-ray research was begun in 1921, there was also initiated a program of research on the problems of high-voltage transmission of electric power. Structural organic chemistry and aeronautical engineering came along next. Later, genetics and jet propulsion—and so on.

Just at this point Caltech and many other institutions face a serious choice. How "pure" can the research program as a whole be and still command community and public support, or how "practical" can it be allowed to become without losing the essential spirit of true scholarship—the search for new knowledge?

There is, of course, no unique answer to this dilemma. Yet every institution must find some answer which is both consistent with its own ideals and consonant with its circumstances and responsibilities.

Our aim at Caltech has been to lean over backward on the side of basic or pure research, and I shall try to explain how we seek to maintain this posture under today's conditions.

Advantages of Small Group

First, we find that a small student body is a prime asset. If our teaching load were allowed to outrun our research capacity, we would then have a large teaching staff inadequately provided with research facilities or funds. The pressure would be great to accept any kind of research task for which funds were made available just to keep the faculty busy. This, you will admit, could lead to unhappy results.

But even under the best circumstances the selection of research activities and research fields remains a critical problem. The momentary glamor of a well-financed but inappropriate project may have to be resisted in favor of the long-term benefits of more basic research activities. To assist in reviewing this situation our faculty and trustees invented the device of a faculty committee on sponsored research. Before an actual proposal for research support can be forwarded to any outside agency, private or government, it must be reviewed by this committee to be sure that it conforms to our ideas of what constitutes basic research. Inasmuch as this committee, with a rotating membership, has been in existence for many years (since 1946), its policies have been well established and are well known to the faculty. It does not often have to veto a project any more. But it has done so, and it can do so at any time.

This does not mean that there have been no "practical" projects. There have been many—even in the basic science fields. For example, a few years ago one of our biochemists, Professor Haagen-Smit, who had had one too many sniffs of the notorious Los Angeles smog, went into his laboratory to see if he could artificially create that characteristic odor. With one eye on the Los Angeles motor traffic and the other on California sunshine, he was soon able to show that gasoline vapor *plus* ultraviolet light did produce a typical smog cloud, and he had soon elucidated the basic ideas of the chemistry of that particular type of air pollution.

Criteria

However, it is in the engineering departments that the most difficult questions arise as to what is fundamental research, what is practical development, and which projects could be more appropriately done in commercial laboratories. Engineering is *applied* science, and engineering research must have some relevance to the practical needs of men. Yet, even here, it is normally possible to distinguish the projects which are aimed toward a basic extension of engineering knowledge and toward new contributions to engineering practice from those which

109

are aimed solely at the perfection of particular devices or techniques. Our computer laboratory does not aim principally at the improvement of computer circuitry, but rather at basically new ways of using the computer as an instrument to solve scientific, engineering, and technical problems, and as a new tool to aid in the development of applied mathematics. The aeronautics laboratory does not design airplanes; it learns about the properties of airflow. And so on.

One useful criterion which helps many decisions in this field is that to be acceptable in any area a research program must be one which is consistent with and contributes to the educational program. This means it must be one in which graduate students can participate. This means, among other things, it must not be "classified," either for reasons of trade secrecy or military security. Also, it must not be one which provides exclusive patent rights to the sponsor. As far as the *on-campus* program is concerned, these rules are now rigidly followed.

Does that mean we have no way of being of service in the field of national defense or industrial development? Not necessarily. When we have found it necessary or desirable—since the close of World War II—to undertake classified activities, they have been done in off-campus installations where restricted access does not inconvenience the teaching program or interrupt the free access to all parts of the campus. We operate two such off-campus installations now: the government-owned Jet Propulsion Laboratory (now the principal laboratory of the National Aeronautics and Space Administration for space flight research) and the Cooperative Wind Tunnel (owned cooperatively by a group of aircraft companies). In both cases Caltech initiated the work of these laboratories during World War II and has continued them ever since under a nonprofit management contract. A number of years ago a temporary classified project was carried on in leased space about two miles from the campus. Thus we are enabled to preserve the condition of free access to all parts of the campus by faculty and students, which we regard as a precious asset not to be relinquished except in times of extreme emergency.

Financing Research Program

How, then, is our basic research program financed?

Here again it must be emphasized that in our case the size of the faculty is determined by the total funds that are available rather than by the number of students to be taken care of. Nevertheless, our able research staff does have an insatiable appetite for more research funds and for continually expanding research programs. Hence, the problems of financing the rapidly rising costs of research and the rapidly growing program are severe indeed.

It may be of interest to list our sources of support. In listing them I shall list support for both teaching and research, for I do not know how to determine at Caltech how many pennies of each dollar go to teaching and how many to research. This is not because our bookkeeping department is inefficient, but only because we purposely mix the two activities so thoroughly that separate budgeting is impossible even *in principle*.

Out of a total *campus* budget of $9 million (in 1957-58), endowment income provided 32 per cent; gifts and grants from nongovernment sources provided 20 per cent; government grants and contracts (including overhead) provided 35 per cent; and tuition and other sources provided 13 per cent. During the past ten years the total budget has doubled. The percentage (but not total volume) of government funds has declined (from 41 to 35 per cent), and of private gifts has risen (from 13.5 to 20 per cent), and the others have remained nearly constant. We hope and expect that these various sources of support will retain the present relative positions in the future, that is, in round numbers: endowment, 30 per cent; gifts, 30 per cent; government contracts, 30 per cent; tuition, 10 per cent. Whether this is just the "right" ratio or not, no one can say. But one can say that maintaining all of these sources of support is of very great importance to any private institution.

It is, of course, just here that all private institutions have a common problem—that of obtaining income from a variety of sources to support both educational and research programs.

There is no question but that the relative importance of endowment income in the private universities has been declining in the nation as a whole. This has sometimes been mistakenly referred to as the "erosion" of endowment funds. Actually, endowment funds have not eroded at all; they have, as a whole, risen rapidly both in book and in market value and they have also increased in their earning power, when properly invested, nearly as fast as prices have risen. Every private institution which has been on its toes has also secured substantial fractional increases in its endowment funds in recent years, and these increases are continuing.

Yet, research and teaching costs have outrun endowment income, not only because the prices of specific products have been inflated, not solely because salaries and wages have risen sharply, but because the equipment, materials, techniques, and manpower for doing research and teaching have changed so greatly. Intricate and enormous machines and instruments, requiring large crews to build and operate them, were almost unknown before the war, even in industrial laboratories. Now they are commonplace.

Clearly, this radical change in research activities has not been financed by endowment funds. The change has been possible only because government funds have been available in substantial amounts. Granted that some government funds have been misplaced and misused; granted that some have been used to support the kinds of things that universities should not be doing; it is still true that government funds have been the backbone of the growth of basic research in the universities in the postwar period. The chief trouble has been that government funds for basic research have not been available in large enough amounts, compared with the funds available for applied research or for testing and developing. It is this fact that has forced many universities to take on development projects in order to have something going on that could be called research. A major problem of the future is to keep these funds for basic research growing at an adequate rate.

Threat of Control through Support

Increasing government support of research raises the question of whether or not the government will assume control of the universities if it provides funds for their research. The chief answer to this question is that it has not happened as yet. The chief threat of control has come not from the government agencies who administer the funds, but from the panels and advisory committees (composed largely of professors!) who pass upon projects and budgets before they are accepted. Many of these groups have steadfastly opposed proper overhead payments on research contracts, have opposed including allowances for the salaries of professors working on the projects, have opposed block or departmental grants, and have required of the prospective research worker such elaborate and detailed proposals and reports that a type of bureaucratic committee control has grown up which suppresses daring ideas and takes administrative control out of the hands of the universities themselves.

All of these things are done with the most pious protestations, of course. "It isn't good for the universities to receive overhead reimbursement and thus become dependent on the government," they say. Or, "It is not good for the professor to have part of his salary paid by the supporter of his research." (Why not? Somebody has to give the university money to pay him.) Again, "Block grants are bad for they put too much power in the hands of the department heads." So a committee in Washington decided *it* is more competent to allocate the funds than the university itself.

As a long-time faculty member myself, I can pray fervently that both I and my faculty may be delivered from dictatorship by government faculty committees. Give me a good smart administrator to deal with and I can dispense with faculty advisory committees, except when they deal with purely scientific affairs and not with administrative or fiscal matters. Scientists, when they get into government, are their own worst enemies. When they have control over activities of their colleagues, through the administration of research grants, they become autocrats of the most difficult kind.

These are serious matters. The rapid rise in research activities has required the universities to expand their plants, their business offices, their maintenance facilities and their libraries. Research grants or contracts which have not borne their share of these costs have been parasites on other sources of funds. It is quite all right to talk about the desirability of the university "sharing the cost" of research with the sponsoring agency. But what with? Endowment funds, as we have said, have scarcely kept pace with rising costs of carrying on the same operations, to say nothing of adding new ones. Corporate executives, I find, get an understandable glassy look in their eyes when they are asked to give money to a university to cover indirect costs of research being sponsored by government agencies because these agencies cannot afford, or are not allowed, or simply refuse, to pay the full costs of the research which they take credit for supporting. Corporations and individuals alike have trouble

114

understanding why they should be asked to underwrite those costs. So, of course, the universities don't ask them to. They ask for "unrestricted funds," or funds for "general support." But of course this is just a euphemistic way of requesting the same thing—money to pay the costs of research which others are pretending to support.

I must say that corporations as a whole have been exceedingly generous in responding to this appeal for unrestricted funds, and this has saved many an institution, including my own, from going broke in recent years. Or rather, I should say, unrestricted corporate support has enabled us to abandon our prohibition against accepting funds from government agencies which do not pay full costs. We now can accept such funds in limited amounts and still remain solvent.

The principal problems in connection with the government support of research are:

1. To increase the funds available for basic research.

2. To persuade all government agencies to pay full costs of the research they support, in spite of contrary advice from their scientific advisory committees (including in full costs the prorated share of the salaries of the faculty members who *do* the research).

3. To enlarge the degree to which block or departmental or general grants are made available for strengthening an *area* of science rather than only a particular project.

4. To persuade the Bureau of the Budget and other fiscal and auditing agencies to modify radically the cost-accounting practices which they now insist upon and which are inappropriate to educational institutions. (With some difficulty I restrain myself from a further discourse on this latter subject, which is even now a subject of strenuous and difficult negotiations between the universities and the government.)

Nongovernment Support

What, then, about the nongovernment sources of support for research in private universities?

The problems here are many, but, though they are not easy, they are not impossible. Granted that the government will continue to support a substantial share of university research—especially the large and expensive projects—private funds still play a critical role. Individuals, corporations and foundations should continue and expand their contributions to endowment funds, operating funds and building funds. Private sources are free to follow the theory that the strength of the basic research program in this nation is primarily dependent on the strength of the institutions that carry on such research. Hence, the most important way to finance research is to finance the institutions—to provide what they need in order to acquire facilities, pay adequate faculty salaries, and maintain the plant in order to attract and support the best research people. Especially is it important to provide the long-term support essential to a real scholarly atmosphere in which new ideas are likely to thrive. New ideas must be born *before* clever and startling research proposals can be submitted to the government. Private funds, wisely given, can enhance the intellectual ferment in our great centers of learning and thus create the environment in which new ideas will arise.

I would not be honest if I did not point out that there are also troubles in the administration of private funds for research. The indirect costs for privately sponsored research are just as great as for government sponsorship. As I have already suggested, the universities have found it embarrassing to pass the hat elsewhere for these costs. So they have done two things: (1) sought more funds—given largely on an annual basis—for "unrestricted" purposes (i.e., to raise salaries and pay overhead), and (2) asked private sponsors of all projects to pay their prorated share of these costs.

Private foundations have been understandably reluctant to do either of these two things. They wish to see their limited funds going for direct, recognizable costs of identifiable projects. Besides, they could point to plenty of institutions where the president or treasurer was a bum but the biology professor was a whizz. They wanted no funds to be diverted from the professor. And obviously, too, their money would "not go as far" if a quarter to a third of it was allocated to indirect costs. "Better to supply 15 hungry men with bread than only 10 with butter too."

I do not pretend to offer any easy formulas for solving this problem. Many foundations and other private agencies have found ways, a variety of ways, to assist. I am only setting forth the problem and ask that we all face the fact that those great research institutions of this country, the private universities, no longer have—if they ever did—"funds of their own" to disperse freely. All their funds are gifts (except, of course, tuition fees). Furthermore, a large share of these gifts now come on an annual basis and not in the form of permanent endowments. Professors on tenure, who resist having their salaries paid partly from project funds because they are on an annual basis, should become aware of the fact that other sources of funds are on an annual basis too and, whether we like it or not, that's the way things are these days. This does not mean the professors will not surely be paid; it only means that *every* possible source of funds must be tapped.

There are some who will bemoan the fact that the universities have allowed themselves to reach such a terrible state. And I admit that universities have been more concerned about national welfare than with their own financial security. The private universities could have pulled in their necks and refused to expand their research until endowment funds had been secured to underwrite it. Some, indeed, did so. But if all had done so and left it to the state universities to become the only research centers, the private university in this country would have been doomed to oblivion. And that would not have been good even for the state universities.

But the private institutions as a whole met the challenge and took the risks. Fortunately, certain of the largest sources of new funds, such as the Office of Naval Research and the U. S. Atomic Energy Commission, did pay full costs for some of the very large university basic research projects which they supported. This helped to keep the universities solvent even though certain other agencies did not pay full costs. Annual unrestricted gifts were sought and found also, and somehow the bills got mostly paid—that is, all were paid except the professors' salaries. *They* had to wait, partly because the professors themselves did not realize the new turn which university financial problems had taken.

If we now raise our eyes from the specific research problems in a specific university to the broader problems of academic research in America, what difficulties do we see? Of course there are many: fiscal, administrative, jurisdictional, political. Some people worry about the "balance" of our research effort— that we will spend too much money on space research and not enough on cancer, or vice versa. (Incidentally, I have frequently seen cases of general agreement on how much is "not enough"; I have never seen a generally accepted way of learning how much is "too much.") Great segments of science and technology now have great popular appeal, and special purpose groups can whip up great enthusiasm for spending huge sums on this disease or that, or on nuclear power, or astronautics or oceanography, or radio astronomy, or other perfectly respectable areas, both basic and applied. Hence, so-called "categorical" funds grow and multiply, both in private and government circles. Of course, one can say that if there are only enough categories, with plenty of funds in each, then full freedom of choice is again available.

But is it?

I shall forever pity the physicist who is anxious to learn about the puzzling behavior of liquid helium II, wasting his time trying to decide whether this is solid state physics or nuclear physics, or maybe oceanography, and whether he should submit proposals to ONR or OOR or NSF. And how can he write a detailed proposal when he is just exploring— when he is just curious?

Fortunately, in precisely this situation and others like it, the Sloan Foundation has indicated that it was interested in supporting inquiring minds, and would be glad to have such minds worry about any questions on earth they pleased.

Here is the great challenge to universities and to all who support them: Are we attracting the cream of the nation's inquiring minds to our campuses, and are we there giving them full encouragement and support in pursuing whatever lines of endeavour interest them, preferably with no questions asked? That is a difficult challenge, possibly an impossible one. But unless we have inquiring minds that are really free to inquire, even in fields outside the cognizance of any Washington or New York committee, then we can never reap the full benefits and satisfactions of free and unfettered scientific research.

As I bring this paper to a close, I realize that I have spent too much time on what seems like dirty administrative problems. I would have enjoyed it much more if I had been describing the magnificent achievements in scientific research the past ten years have witnessed. From the center of the earth to outer space; from the nucleus of the atom to the nucleus of the cell; from the theory of solids to the evolution of the universe; from the structure of proteins to the geography of Antarctica; from cybernetics to astronautics, great new areas of science have seen astonishing advances. Thousands of young men and women have found fruitful and satisfying careers in scientific research and America's universities, private and public, have become national assets of prime importance, not only because they aid in the advance of welfare and security but also because they are the congenial homes of the inquiring minds, the great stimulators and supporters of that restless and adventurous thing, the human spirit.

CAPSULE CONCLUSIONS

J. R. KILLIAN, JR.
Special Assistant to the President
for Science and Technology

M Y REMARKS are limited to a ten-min-
ute capsule of conclusions and observations drawn from a year-
and-a-half's work and experience by the President's Science
Advisory Committee. The President has afforded us an unprecedented opportunity to inform ourselves and to marshal
from across the land scientific advice for the government. He
has instructed us to evaluate, and to be available for information
and advice on science and technology as they affect national
security and the general welfare and on ways science may be
strengthened and encouraged within and without government.

In support of this assignment, we have completed during
the past eighteen months thirty-seven major studies and reports
conducted by twenty-seven panels, utilizing the experience and
knowledge of 160 outstanding scientists and engineers recruited
from industry, education, and government. About half of these
studies have dealt with ways through which science and
engineering can support our national security objectives,
but some of the most extensive studies have been directed at
the strengthening of science and engineering in the United
States and the Free World.

From this wide range of review and inquiry, and without stopping to give credit to individual reports, I draw the following four categories of observations and conclusions which bear upon the efficient use of manpower and resources over the whole spectrum of research and development.

The first has to do with our progress and position in science and engineering. American science has a scope and depth unequaled at present anywhere in the world. Today we are technologically strong and are growing stronger. I do not believe that we have lost our technological leadership or that we are predestined to lose it in the future. But with all our present strength, we have work to do and weaknesses to correct to underwrite our future strength and to realize our own full potential. My next three groups of observations emphasize some of the requirements we must meet to continue strong.

There is, for example, the requirement for better balance and proportion in our national research and development program. Of the government's total research and development budget, about 6 per cent is earmarked for basic research. The remaining pays for applied research and the development of an almost endless list of "things," such as jet planes, missiles, nuclear reactors, satellites, insecticides, vaccines, drugs, rocket fuels, computers, and space suits. Since the Korean War, the amount of money for the development of "things" has increased more, in proportion, than the funds available for basic research. Happily, in the past year-and-a-half, basic research has been gaining. It is not that more funds are needed for the whole range of research and development. We need a more balanced distribution.

Another kind of research has also been undernourished. I refer to "analytical engineering" or applied or supporting research—the sophisticated scrutiny of available knowledge to determine what sort of "things" are possible to build and which are not, and what may be the magnitude of their cost. It is obvious to everyone familiar with development of hardware that the design of "things" is handicapped at every turn by a lack of basic knowledge and for want of definition of that which can be created within the limits of present knowledge. While difficult to prove, there is little doubt that a more vigorous support of basic research—and "analytical engineering"—could pay rich dividends in making "things" easier and less costly to develop, especially less costly in manpower. It also would minimize the need for expensive crash programs. It could help in preventing premature production.

Recently Mr. Kappel, President of the American Telephone and Telegraph Company, expressed a similar conclusion about the importance of such research in industry when he said: "The cost of development is far greater than the cost of research, and if a big development gets off on the wrong foot, the price is terribly high."

The need for additional basic and supporting research is nowhere more evident than in those technological developments which require new materials or materials with new and unique properties, as for example, in the design of advanced nuclear reactors. Some of our technology has been limited because we have not yet achieved the necessary mastery over materials. It has frequently been necessary to engineer around inadequate materials, thus greatly increasing the cost of a project. For want of improved materials, some projects have been unable to meet specifications, and even others have failed of accomplishment.

My third category of observations relates to problems in the management of our technology. There is sometimes a tendency, for example, to overcomplicate and overelaborate the technological products and systems that we produce. This is always a temptation in the development of military weapons, but this practice is not limited to military technology. Most modern weapons, even in their simplest form, must be enormously complex; but we need to resist the temptation to add to this complexity through a prodigal use of our technological resources. It frequently proves that in an "all out" effort to develop a given weapons system, we tend to multiply the requirements on the system, thereby adding to its complexity and to the time and cost required for development. As one of my associates recently remarked, we have become in too many instances "technology happy," too much preoccupied with technological spit and polish, too little concerned with disciplined, tough-minded design and control, and have given too little attention to simplicity, operational practicality and reliability, and early completion.

There is also today a tendency to let the spectacular aspects of some kinds of technology lead us to give undue attention to those things which are glamorous, at the expense of those things which are important and badly needed. As we push ahead with the military uses of outer space and the advanced technology of space science and exploration, as indeed we are and must, and as we pursue glamorous technological objectives in other fields, let us not forget that we have vitally important, if less spectacular, programs in military technology and in science that must not be downgraded in the emphasis we give them and in the top-flight manpower we assign to them.

I do not imply that we should be any less bold or audacious, any less far-reaching and creative in our technology. I do suggest that we have problems of common-sense priority and funding and use of scientists and engineers which require disciplined judgment in our planning and in establishing requirements. Research, especially applied research, can help provide the critical analysis necessary to define meaningful priorities.

One of the rarest types of managerial talent today is that

which comprehends the problems, both human and technological, in the building of huge complex systems and is competent
effectively to coordinate the elements of research, development,
test, and production required in the achievement of a system.
Those programs which have been most successful in the development of these complicated systems, whether they be for
defense or for nonmilitary application, have usually been successful because their program managers are capable not only
of handling the problems involving organization and people,
but also comprehend, with loving attention to detail, every element of the system. We have a dire shortage of this kind of
talent.

My final set of observations relates to the role of education in advancing our science and technology. This role is
crucial, and much must be done from grammar school through
graduate school to better our education. At present, however,
one of our most pressing needs is to strengthen and expand
graduate education in science and engineering.

In a report just made to the new Federal Council for
Science and Technology, a panel on materials research cited the
lack of highly trained scientific manpower as the real limitation
on the development of this important field. The panel pointed
to the urgent need for more and better basic research with more
and better people doing it. They strongly urged that ways be
found in our colleges and universities to increase materials research facilities, especially interdisciplinary laboratories, in order
to educate more men who can make creative contributions to
this field.

In the past fifty years graduate education in the sciences
has come to maturity in the United States. We have a few
centers of great distinction—as distinguished as any to be found
in the world—but we have too few of these and only a handful
that excel in more than one field of science. We need more top-

flight graduate schools of science with more top-flight departments.

We should have twice as many first-rate graduate schools of engineering as we now have. At the last count we were producing only about 600 doctor's degrees in engineering each year, and this is not enough.

It is important both to multiply and to strengthen our schools of engineering. The need is to recognize the heightened level of versatility which is necessary for the engineer today and to increase the scientific depth of our engineering education.

And now with this brief report before you, may I close with a general observation. In the face of the practical responsibilities which rest in science and engineering for our security and our national welfare, let us not forget that science has a deeper cultural importance and a deeper motivation. It attracts first-rate minds because it yields adventure, insight, and understanding. It is one of man's most powerful and noble means for searching out truth and for enhancing man's dignity by augmenting his understanding. If science is thus understood, we will have accomplished a major requirement for achieving a high level of creative accomplishment and for maintaining a vigorous and advancing technology.

BASIC RESEARCH:
A TECHNOLOGICAL
SAVINGS ACCOUNT

CRAWFORD H. GREENEWALT
E. I. du Pont de Nemours & Company

I SHOULD like first to congratulate the sponsoring organizations for their wisdom and foresight in planning this *Symposium on Basic Research*. I must also pay tribute to Mr. Alfred Sloan whose keen interest has provided the principal stimulus for this meeting. Mr. Sloan has been revered for many years as one of our great industrial statesmen. It is most gratifying to have him devote his talents and energies also to the world of science.

I can think of no more important question for searching appraisal than the adequacy, diversity, and magnitude of our basic research effort. In applied research, this country is pre-eminent. We need bow to no other nation in our ability to turn scientific discovery into goods and services for the benefit of mankind. Research and development expenditures, public and private, totaled about ten billion dollars in 1957, and even this great sum can be amply justified in terms of steadily improving living standards and an increasingly impregnable national security.

Applied research and development, however, are concerned primarily with the present. For the future, we must place our reliance on basic research, which is to say the new discoveries in pure science which will support applied research in the years to come.

We might liken our pool of basic scientific knowledge to a savings account from which we make withdrawals as we convert that knowledge through applied research to new products and processes. As with all savings accounts, bankruptcy lies ahead when withdrawals exceed deposits. To keep our scientific balance in healthy condition, we must insure always that our deposits derived from basic research are never less than our technological withdrawals.

Certainly no one can take issue with the necessity for basic research, for to do so would be to deny the impact of human creativity on our spiritual and material well being. Each step forward in man's progress can be traced back to a flash of creative genius in the mind of some gifted individual. To him the utility of his brain child is far less important than his success in penetrating to some small degree the dark curtains of our ignorance. I am reminded of my friend, Professor Edgerton of Massachusetts Institute of Technology, who has been attempting to photograph the ocean floor at depths of several miles. Someone asked him what he expected to find and what use he expected to make of his observations. He replied, "If I knew, I wouldn't do it."

Were it necessary to justify in material terms each effort at new discovery, I doubt that there would be room in our society for basic research or, in fact, for individual creativity in any form. Had Newton to justify his work on universal gravitation to a profit-minded board of directors, I suspect that the falling apple would have given him no more than an unpleasant bump on the head. Had Shakespeare to guarantee a paying audience for each of his plays, I doubt that we would have known *Hamlet* or *Romeo*. Had Beethoven to justify his music on the basis of popular approval, he would have left us nothing.

The support of creativity in any area is nothing more than an affirmation of our faith in man's intellectual capacity. It is, in fact, only that capacity that sets humanity apart from the beasts in the field and forest. If we are not prepared to support creativity, we are not prepared to support ourselves.

All of this is surely obvious, and I have no doubt that all can agree on the importance of basic research and, in fact, on any other manifestation of the creative process. The problem, it seems to me, is quantitative—not qualitative. Basic research must surely be done. The question is one of scale and how best to marshal our forces in its support.

Traditionally, basic research has been the responsibility of the universities, and it is from their laboratories and faculties in this country and abroad that we have in the past received the seeds of knowledge which have grown and matured into our present industrial establishment.

In industry, even applied research was a novelty prior to the present century, and one can only marvel at its extraordinary growth during a period well within the life span of most of us here.

More recently, many companies have undertaken basic research with their own personnel and in their own laboratories. The Du Pont Company, for example, initiated such a program in 1927 with a modest budget and a handful of scientists. Today our expenditures for basic research exceed fifteen million dollars annually, a sum equal to our entire research expenditures not many years ago. Many companies in many industries have instituted similar programs. Indeed, industrial research in this area is nothing more than a recognition by management of its responsibility to insure corporate longevity.

Fundamental research in industry has also resulted in

greater cooperation, understanding, and respect between industrial and academic scientists. Today industrial scientists at
meetings of learned societies rub elbows on equal terms with
their academic associates. In the *Journal* and at the meetings of
the American Chemical Society, the percentage of papers presented by industrial authors is increasing steadily. I suspect that
this is true also in other fields. The use of academic consultants
in industrial research has increased greatly in recent years.

This intermingling of industrial and academic scientists
has created a warm and fruitful relationship for both and has,
I am sure, done much to forward the cause of basic research.

These developments are encouraging, but I do not mean
to imply that basic research in industry will keep our aggregate
effort at a sufficiently high level. In fact, I am quite certain that
it will not, and that basic research, particularly in the universities, must be greatly expanded and diversified.

In industry, basic research must of necessity be restricted
to fields which are at least of potential commercial interest.
Du Pont, for example, can profitably undertake such research
in the fields of high polymers or organic chemistry, but it would
be difficult for us to justify research in oceanography, for
example, or in astronomy, or in paleontology. These areas and
many others are inevitably the province of the universities, and
means must be found to make sure that their exploration will
be aggressively pursued.

In such disciplines, the significance of new discovery can
never be predicted or justified on the basis of utility or profit-
ability. Nonetheless, one can be certain that new knowledge
is never wasted, that someday, somehow, it can be turned to the
benefit of mankind. We can be sure also that today no area of
science stands alone, that more and more, important new discoveries are the result of a synthesis of contributions from many
seemingly unrelated disciplines. The support of what might be

called uncommitted fundamental research must be a matter of faith. It is a faith that can be amply justified in the certainty that new knowledge will one day be valuable, whatever its form, whatever its direction.

The financial support of academic research, it seems to me, is a clear responsibility of industry and government, not as an act of altruism, but to provide an insurance policy, if you will, for future progress. I am glad to note that both industry and government are meeting that obligation in their increasing support of academic research. I would say only that what is being done is still inadequate, and that private and public agencies should increase substantially their contributions to basic research in university laboratories.

I believe also that neither industry nor government has fully realized the importance of the unrestricted grant, the type of grant that recognizes the quality and ability of the scientist as distinct from the general appeal of the program for which he asks support.

The Du Pont Company has, over the last ten years, made such unrestricted grants to many universities aggregating several million dollars. We require no justification, no program or project. We look only at the quality of the man, the department, or the university to which the grant is made.

Too often a university scientist is forced to compromise, to modify, or to restrict his program in order that he may prepare a project sufficiently attractive to win the support of a sponsor. It seems to me that public and private agencies should have sufficient confidence to support talent without restriction, indeed without any basis other than confidence in the inherent ability of the individual.

In sum, I would urge a substantial increase in unrestricted funds, based not upon projects but on men, not upon desired objectives but upon creative talent. Only in this way can we be sure that no fruitful path will remain untraveled, no brain child will die from lack of nourishment, no genius whose ideas are allowed to atrophy.

Our nation has reached its present high stature because of an underlying faith in individual accomplishment. Basic research is first of all people and ideas, not products or objectives, and it should be supported on precisely those terms. With adequate faith and adequate support, I am certain that our technological savings account will not be overdrawn.

SCIENCE:
HANDMAIDEN
OF FREEDOM

DWIGHT D. EISENHOWER
The White House

IT IS a great privilege to be present at this meeting with so many Americans actively interested in basic science. Equally it is for me a unique experience. I have no professional competence in searching out nature's secrets and out of my own knowledge I can make no professional suggestions, on the substance of science, to which you could possibly accord the slightest validity.

Nevertheless, I hope that in a fairly long life, punctuated here and there by promotions of various types, that I have not reached the state of exalted position and complete uselessness that was achieved by one of the hunting dogs I heard about, trained by a northern woodsman. Their master, who had long enjoyed a warm acquaintanceship with a university community, had the habit of naming his dogs for faculty members that he admired. But when a few wives became a little indignant over the practice, he decided to name his dogs for various academic ranks—instructor, assistant, and professor, and so on.

One hunting season, a man from Chicago hired for two dollars and a half a day a dog he liked very much. The following year, when he asked for the same dog, he was told the price would be five dollars a day. When he protested the steep inflation and insisted that it was the same dog, the owner agreed but said that the dog had been promoted to assistant professor and was now worth the added money. The next hunting season, the price jumped to seven dollars and a half because the dog had then achieved the rank of associate professor, and the year after, it was raised to ten dollars, the reason being that the well-trained canine had reached the noble status of full professor.

The following year, when the hunter returned to rent the same dog, he was turned down. "Why not?" demanded the hunter insistently. "Well, I'll tell you," said the old woodsman, "I can't let you have him at any price. This spring we gave him another promotion and made him the president of the college. Now all he does is sit around and howl and bark, and he ain't worth shooting."

Now, even though my scientific education is limited, I think there may be some usefulness in considering together certain aspects of the relation of government to science and the conditions under which the work of scientists and scholars will best flourish.

In our lifetime greater advances have probably taken place in science and technology than in all prior history, and these advances have profoundly affected, and will continue to affect, our manner of living. These advances and changes have also had a profound effect on government and on national policy. In my public service I have found myself increasingly involved in dealing with problems and policies affected by the growth and impact of science and technology. Out of this experience in dealing with these matters and my close and cordial relationships with increasing numbers of scientists and engineers arise such observations as I shall make here.

First, I must congratulate the Sloan Foundation, the National Academy of Science, and the American Association for the Advancement of Science, for sponsoring this conference on basic research. The nation cannot help but feel a profound satisfaction in seeing so many leading representatives of education, industry, and government participating in a symposium concerned with such a vital effort. I derive special satisfaction from the fact that this conference is sponsored by private interests. Too often we have tended to look unduly to the federal government for initiative and support in a multitude of activities, among them scientific research. We must recognize the possibility that the federal government, with its vast resources and its increasing dependence upon science, could largely preempt the field or blunt private initiative and individual opportunity. This we must never permit. Too much dependence upon the federal government may be easy, but too long practiced it can become a dangerous habit.

Yet, government's role in research and its responsibility for advancing science must be large and there must be a persistent partnership between government effort and private effort. Our science and technology are the cornerstone of American security, American welfare and our program for a just peace. For the government to neglect this would be folly. But the strength, growth, and vitality of our science and engineering, as in every other productive enterprise, hinge primarily upon the efforts of private individuals.

Private institutions, foundations, colleges, and universities, professional societies and industry, as well as all levels of government, have a vital role to play in promoting individual leadership and in striving for excellence and the achievements of a high level of creative activity. Thus is created increased opportunity to pioneer, to initiate, and to explore untrodden areas.

135

Freedom and Scientific Knowledge

Through the growth of scientific knowledge we in America have profited immeasurably. We have done so because we are free. Freedom is the central concept of our society, and this freedom of each to try, to fail, and to try again is the mainspring of our progress.

Freedom is both cause and effect; by sustaining it we preserve the essential condition of learning, while the benefits that flow from knowledge work to keep us free. As we have long known, freedom must be earned and protected every day by every one of us. Freedom bestows on us the priceless gift of opportunity—if we neglect our opportunities we shall certainly lose our freedom.

Our immediate task, America's first responsibility, is to see that freedom is not lost through ignorance, complacency, or lack of vigilance. This applies both to our domestic problems and to those abroad. It is important that in our daily lives at home we so conduct ourselves in politics, in business, in education that liberty is not impaired. Equally, we must be alert to our duty of assuring that neither we nor other free nations succumb to an ideological system dedicated to aggressive force and governed by fear.

That we succeed in this task—that we successfully preserve freedom amidst an uneasy climate of disquiet and tension —depends more than ever upon the readiness of each of us to advance American science and engineering. It is in this strong conviction that I particularly stress the freedom of the scholar and the researcher.

The Tradition to Promote Learning

From the very outset of our Republic, the government of the United States has sought to encourage science and learning.

Our early statesmen, Washington, Jefferson, Franklin, and Adams, all sought to find ways by which the new Republic could sponsor learning and promote the progress of science and the useful arts. The founders of the American political system clearly believed that the secrets of nature must be better known so that they might be used to advance the welfare of all our people.

While, under the stimulus of practical need, the application of science to problems of production and growth became accepted practice in our young, vigorous, and rapidly growing society, the uninformed often referred in slurring terms to what they called the "impractical scholar." Fortunately, we have come far from that point. We have done much in overcoming this misunderstanding. We have learned that the apparently visionary researcher is likely to produce unexpectedly practical results. Witness the work of such scientists as Faraday, Pasteur, Gibbs, Einstein, Fermi, and von Neumann.

Basic science, of course, is the essential underpinning of applied research and development. It represents the frontier where exploration and discovery begin. Moreover, achievements in basic research, adding as they do to man's fundamental understanding, have a quality of universality that goes beyond any limited or local application or limitation of time. Eventually, those discoveries benefit all mankind.

Today, the American record in basic research is becoming no less brilliant than in applied science. The past fifty years have seen a remarkable growth of graduate schools of science and other types of research institutions. Since World War II scientists working in the United States have won more than half of all the Nobel prizes awarded in the physical sciences. If we can continue to cultivate our strength and achievement in this field of basic research, we shall greatly enhance our capacity to defend ourselves, and simultaneously advance our economic and cultural strength. Vigilance and effort are required.

I am told that fewer than 30,000 scientists and engineers, or less than two hundredths of one per cent of our population, are now engaged in basic research. Only about four per cent of our scientists and engineers are engaged in basic research. Educators and scientists warn us that we need to step up this effort, if we are to move forward on the broadest scientific front. I think that this has to be a studied effort. Although we have long known that necessity is the mother of invention, we cannot depend upon accident to bring about these advances that we need.

All of us know the old story of finding that cooked meat was much better than raw meat, when the ancient Chinese had his barn burned down and a bunch of pigs were in it. Well, he found out about crackling—that it was very good.

Another accident, and for this story I am indebted to a friend of mine here who is far too shy and modest to want me to identify him. This man needed a hearing aid, and he went to the store and he found that the cheapest one was two hundred dollars. When he learned they ran up to eight hundred, he decided this was clearly outside his pocketbook range and so he decided to make one himself—which he did, and he worked it with pretty good effect.

Finally, a man said to him, "Now tell me, Bill, does this thing really work?"

He answered, "Of course not, but it makes everybody talk louder."

We cannot afford to look for our advances in this kind of result, even if the result was, in this case, only psychological.

In seeking out and educating the necessary talent we need to insure, as we have done in the past, that the search for fundamental knowledge can best be undertaken in areas and in ways determined primarily by the scientific community itself. We reject a philosophy that emphasizes more dependence upon a centralized approach and direction. Regimented research would be, for us, catastrophe.

The progress and growth of America depends upon many qualities of our people. Clearly these include curiosity, imagination, educational preparedness, and tireless stamina. Without these we could not be a people of true creative genius. We must search out the talented individual and cultivate in all American life a heightened appreciation of the importance of excellence and high standards, not only in specialized fields but in individual dimensions of diversity as well.

It is very much worth noting Tocqueville's comment of one hundred twenty-five years ago, in some notes just published for the first time, that what makes the American such an intelligent citizen is that he does a little of everything. This he thought was an important reason for superiority of the American in the ordinary business of life and the government of society.

But while today we require a high degree of specialization, it remains vitally important for the specialist in every field to understand that his first responsibility to himself and to his country is to be a good citizen. Above all, the specialist must comprehend how his own work fits in effectively in promoting the national welfare.

Government Financial Support

Twenty years ago, federal support of science was about one hundred million dollars annually. Today, this annual investment, by the federal government, in applied and basic research, together with pilot development, has grown to over five billion dollars. A large fraction of these federal funds is spent in laboratories owned and operated by private groups.

Much of this expenditure is to meet the current and practical needs of the federal government. The size of these federal expenditures and the policies and practices of the federal government inevitably have a substantial effect on the nation's private scientific institutions. But again we remind ourselves that the whole program would be self-defeating if it were allowed to limit the freedom of its own research.

During recent months we have made many moves to strengthen the management of your government's scientific activities. These include a number of advisory committees and several new legally authorized agencies; all are designed to point up and enhance and coordinate scientific research.

Now, let me cite one example which illustrates an appropriate way for the federal government to further our basic scientific research effort. Recently the General Advisory Committee to the Atomic Energy Commission and my Science Advisory Committee, under the chairmanship of Dr. Killian, appointed a special panel of scientists to undertake a comprehensive review of the federal government's participation in the high-energy accelerator physics field.

On the basis of this report, I am recommending to the Congress that the federal government finance the construction as a national facility of a large new electron linear accelerator. Physicists consider the project, which has been sponsored by Stanford University, to be of vital importance. Moreover, they believe it promises to make valuable contributions to our understanding in a field in which the United States already is strong, and in which we must maintain our progress. Because of the cost, such a project must become a federal responsibility. This proposed national facility, which will be by far the largest of its kind ever built—a machine two miles long—has the endorsement of the interested government agencies—including the

Treasury. Construction of the accelerator will take six years, at an over-all cost of approximately $100,000,000.

Our Goals

By such means the government labors to advance our scientific knowledge and to further the free use of science for healing, for enriching life, and freeing the spirit. In emphasizing these objectives and needs, I am deeply aware that they are inseparable from the broader goal of enriching the quality of our society and enhancing the excellence of our intellectual life.

We cannot improve science and engineering education without strengthening education of all kinds. America must educate all the varied talents of our citizens to the limit of their abilities. Here what we seek is talent of the first rank. We do not ask of a man his race, his color, his religion. In the field of intellectual exploration, true freedom can and must be practiced.

The dignity of man is enhanced by the dignity and freedom of learning. How well the learning is accomplished depends upon the competence and devotion of those to whom the training is entrusted: the teachers and educators at all levels, everywhere, throughout our land. So let us cultivate more respect for learning, for intellectual achievement, for appreciation of the arts and humanities. Let us assign true education a top place among our national goals. This means that we must be willing to match our increasing investments in material resources with increasing investments in men.

For my part I have long urged and supported the idea that there should be established a hall of fame for the Arts and Sciences. Membership would be an honor to which every American boy and girl could aspire.

141

Talent and quality are vital to our national strength—they are the ingredients needed to carry us onward and upward to higher peaks of achievement in science as well as in the non-material world of the mind and the spirit.

Science, great as it is, remains always the servant and the handmaiden of freedom. And a free science will ever be one of the most effective tools through which man will eventually bring to realization his age-old aspiration for an abundant life, with peace and justice for all.

Basic Research in GOVERNMENT LABORATORIES

ALLEN V. ASTIN
National Bureau of Standards

Introduction

FOR MOST of my talk I shall use a special definition of basic research. This definition differs somewhat from the customary ones used in classifying research, but I believe it has a special relevance to the requirements of government laboratories. I plan also to use some statistical data relevant to basic research in government laboratories, and these data have been compiled according to the definitions established by the National Science Foundation. I doubt, however, that the points I hope to make would be altered significantly if I were able to use statistical data based upon my definition.

Research itself is of the nature of inquiry. Inquiry is, in fact, the fundamental characteristic of the activity. We ask of an event or phenomenon, its properties, its structure, its meaning, and its causes. We inquire as to the relationships among various events or phenomena. Sometimes we inquire of our relation to the event or phenomena. We ask of ourselves: Do we see it as it is? How do we err in our observation? Can we reproduce the event or phenomenon? Inquiry is the heart of all scientific research.

Now, what is meant by basic research? Of course, it is a class of this inquisitive activity. It is characterized, I believe, only by the intensity or depth of the inquiry. We consider, then, the degree to which the researcher explores the event or phenomenon and the clarity with which he examines his own procedures and observations. Thus, when I speak of basic research I speak of an inquisitive scientific activity which gives the investigator the right to question all aspects of the data, the procedure, and the interpretation. The investigator is thus free, in fact is encouraged, to pursue a line inquiry to the outer edge of knowledge. To the extent that he does so, he is engaging in basic research. The foundation for basic research becomes a frame of mind, limited by intelligence and talent, from which comes a continuous challenge to authority to prove itself and an alertness for new and better explanations of things as they are.

You can see how difficult is the position of the basic researcher under such a definition. Everything we know is inadequate. Everything we do should be done better. Everything we accept could be understood more fully. The basic researcher in science is today in an unusually difficult position. He must undertake his inquiry under conditions peculiar to our technological age, an age in which science is valued principally for political-utilitarian-economic effects and much less for its intellectuality. In such an age, the basic researcher has found his right of inquiry justified in somewhat unrealistic terms.

I know this to be true especially when it comes to basic research in government laboratories. The government basic researcher is a part of a larger structure devoted to some social good. His activities are justified, and rightly so, to administrators and legislators in terms of his ultimate contribution to society and of some sure-to-come practical benefit. The right of inquiry and the depth of the search are sometimes alluded to, but only as a passing reference to scientific complexity rather than to the fundamental search of man.

But I am getting ahead of my story. Let us agree that one may look on research as a frame of mind which is always questioning what is known and always seeking to know something better. And the research becomes more basic as we extend our questioning closer to the frontier of understanding. Such activity is vital to government laboratory programs, whether such programs be primarily research, application, testing, or evaluation. This is the argument of this talk. It will come as no surprise to you that I consider basic research as essential to government laboratories, but it may be a variation of your awareness of our need to understand that I consider that basic research may be applied to almost all our laboratory responsibilities whether they be scientifically esoteric or so-called routine evaluation.

My talk is limited to basic research in government laboratories. I will stress the special requirements of these laboratories. We have our unique responsibilities and our special problems. It is therefore logical to expect that, although government laboratories share a number of problems, needs, and experiences with other scientific organizations, they also have specific needs related to their special roles.

Problem of Placement of Research

I might say at this point that basic research activities are only one of the special problems of government laboratories. Another general problem which the government now faces is the establishment of criteria for the placement of research. Should a given research program be placed in a government laboratory or in a nongovernment institution? One aspect of

145

this general problem is that of the placement of specific basic research projects. I note this in passing, but shall not offer any extended discussion on this point.

I believe it would be useful in dealing with the problem of basic research in government laboratories if I were to provide some descriptive background about the nature and origins of government laboratories. When you consider that today the government operates more than one hundred laboratories, many of which estimate staff sizes by thousands, you become aware of the commitment to science of the federal agencies in terms of facilities, equipment, and personnel. Of course, the extent of this commitment is chiefly a characteristic of the last quarter century of our history. Prior to the Civil War, the government's interest in science was limited to the observational and collecting activities of a few federal institutions. The work of the Coast and Geodetic Survey, the Naval Observatory, and the Smithsonian Institution deserve special mention. In the period leading up to the turn of the nineteenth century, government science programs became active in a number of other federal organizations, notably the Geological Survey, the Weather Bureau, and the newly established Department of Agriculture. By World War I, the National Bureau of Standards had a fifteen-year-old research program in operation and a number of military laboratories had been established.

Before World War I, the federal research programs may be characterized as follows. They were principally in-house programs performed by government scientists. They were oriented to meet the immediate problems of the agency or of a particular segment of society which the agency serves. Projects which were undertaken were supposed to be of direct applicability to an operating mission assigned to the parent agency. For example, agriculture research activities of laboratories of the Department of Agriculture were directed to meet the daily problems of the farm and the farm-products processor. Similarly, the early projects undertaken by the National Bureau of Standards were industrially oriented. Fully balanced laboratory research programs were usually not possible. Nor did planners deem it necessary to invest a portion of staff time in fundamental studies.

World War I and the accompanying scientific situation altered this condition. That war indicated that this country must achieve a high degree of scientific self-sufficiency. We could no longer rely on European science for its observations, its data, and its theorizing. In the 1920's and 1930's government scientific laboratories tried to overcome this reliance on foreign research. Fuller and more adequate technical programs were proposed and partially activated. Nonetheless, the degree of support provided to federal science was inadequate to meet any criterion of self-sufficiency. In World War II, these government laboratories were in a somewhat more able position to meet America's urgent problems, but these laboratories were far from adequate for the large-scale technical problems faced by that war. So we were introduced to the broad contract research which is now so familiar to modern government science. One thing you must note in all this. Government science programs developed in spurts and under the pressure of emergencies. It is not surprising that present government laboratories have some difficulty in winning acceptance of planned-for long-range research programs which will include basic research.

Today, as I have said, there are more than one hundred major government laboratories. Most of these are in the physical sciences. A very high percentage of these is involved in military programs. They may be classified according to their function or the types of service they provide. Some are involved in data compilation and data dissemination, such as the Weather Bureau, the Geological Survey, and the Bureau of the Census.

Some are involved in providing the technical bases for regulatory activities of the government, such as the Food and Drug Administration, and the Public Health Service. Some are involved in providing technical assistance, advice, and information as a service to science and the general welfare, such as the laboratories of the Department of Agriculture, the National Bureau of Standards, and the National Institutes of Health. By far the largest number are serving the needs of the Department of Defense, such as the Naval Research Laboratory, the Fort Monmouth Signal Laboratories, and the Wright-Patterson Air Development Center.

Federal Expenditures
in Government Laboratories

During the years since World War II, the investment in such laboratory activities has increased. Without dwelling too much on expenditure statistics, I would like to make a few general observations. The federal government provides about half the funds for the support of research and development in this country. Within government laboratories, less than 20 per cent of the research and development activities are conducted. The federal government provides more than one-third of the funds for the support of basic research in this country. Within government laboratories, a little over 10 per cent of the basic research activities are conducted. I think that it is significant to note that the government performs in its own laboratories almost a third of the total basic research for which it pays. I have no quarrel with this. It seems to me that government laboratories get a fair share, percentage-wise, of the federal monies made available for fundamental studies. If I have a quarrel it is with the total percentage of research and development funds available for basic research. Less than 10 per cent of the total research and development effort goes to basic

148

research, and this is not enough. I am aware that there is a need to appreciate that the federal science budget is only a part of the total federal budget, but it seems to me that within any limitation set on federal science expenditures the percentage made available for basic research should be greater. I believe that this should be the case even if it means restricting some urgent development activities. I believe that in the long run the nation and the nation's science will benefit from investments on a higher percentage level in basic research.

This higher percentage investment in basic research will have important secondary effects on the work of government laboratories. If government laboratories continue to perform about one-third of the basic activities that are financed with federal funds, then the absolute amount available for in-house fundamental studies will increase. This will also influence significantly the programs of federal laboratories. For with more money available for basic research in government institutions, federal agencies will be encouraged to contract out to industry for some of the applied research and almost all development activities now performed by government scientists. Thus there would be achieved a realignment with a heavier weighting toward basic research in federal laboratories. This would mean that eventually there would be a shifting toward basic research in government laboratories and a shifting of development to industry. I believe that all government laboratories would benefit from such a shift, including government laboratories of the Department of Defense.

Because I feel strongly about this point, let me summarize it here. First, there should be a conscious policy and strong effort to increase the percentage of federal science funds devoted to basic research. Second, federal laboratories should increase their conduct of basic research and contract out for more of their development activities.

It is important that all government scientific laboratories become more active in basic research. This seems consistent with a fundamental responsibility of government to foster science in this country. It is characteristic of government activities that they provide a general good for the national community and a service upon which various segments of society may call. In this respect, an increase in the level of government laboratory basic research may be considered a technical service to the scientific community which, in turn, serves the nation as a whole.

Research Information Programs

These basic activities of federal laboratories are associated with and complemented by other general services provided by the government. I spoke earlier of the data compilation and disseminating functions of government institutions. Here we have another example of a technical service to the scientific community and to the nation. It is now recognized that the government has a substantial stake in the progress of science and that there are a number of things which it can do to improve the rate of progress. Among these are the data dissemination activities. More and more, federal institutions are becoming actively engaged in the research information programs of the nation. Now, I do not call this "basic research" (although there is a great need for more basic research on this subject), but it is an important activity in the service of basic research because it improves the yield and the consistency of these fundamental studies. In the case of the National Bureau of Standards, for example, I am aware of and impressed by the seminal effect which Bureau-published tables and data collections have on research in other laboratories. I think this type of effort is one of the most important things that government laboratories can do to create improved national conditions for basic research.

Basic Research Relation to Other Activities

In addition to these general responsibilities which government laboratories have and which are served by in-house basic research programs, there is a specific relationship between such basic activities and the missions assigned to government laboratories. It should be noted that no federal laboratory, with the possible exception of The Smithsonian Institution, exists just to undertake programs of a basic scientific nature. Each laboratory has been established to serve the assigned responsibilities of the parent agency. Or in the case of an independent agency such as NACA, recently absorbed into NASA, its establishment was to meet a practical need. Its charter authorized a "study of the problems of flight *with a view to their practical solution.*" In this context, there can be no question of the propriety of undertaking research projects directed at fulfilling authorized responsibilities. But how does one justify basic research projects under such conditions? I believe that such basic activities are proper for the following compelling reasons: First, basic research, as defined earlier, should not be separated from other research activity. Second, basic research increases the competence to undertake and improve all research activities. And third, basic research in government identifies the government with an implicit responsibility of government to society.

Let me elaborate on each of these points very briefly. Basic research should not be divorced from other research activities. We are deluding ourselves if we attempt to make a separation in some exact way. All research partakes of this questioning that I have spoken of earlier. To the degree that we encourage questioning in depth, to that degree do we permit ourselves the necessity of basic research.

I have come in contact with projects which have been called routine testing or mere evaluation. And those projects have suffered by this name calling. The result has been that the personnel engaged in the work have ceased to explore and the possibilities for critical improvements have been radically reduced. If, on the other hand, a basic interest is encouraged and applied to such problems, there is an enhancement of understanding and a resultant increase of technical efficiency.

Competence of Personnel

This leads to the second point. Basic research leads to increased competence. I have no statistics to prove this, but I am certain that there is a direct correlation between the level of basic activity in a laboratory and its general competence. The quality of a laboratory staff is its most important resource. Quality of staff is eminent in its priority over equipment, funds, and facilities. In government laboratories, the quality of the personnel is a most abused resource. I shall have more to say on "abuse" shortly, but here it is pertinent to relate quality to output and the authorized mission of the laboratory. If that mission is to be pursued with vigor and imagination, if the laboratory is to accept its assignment in its full significance, then it must have the talent capable of exercising creative judgment. No laboratory can maintain productivity in research without high-quality personnel. No laboratory can retain first-rate personnel without permitting the right and freedom of basic questioning. These two statements complement each other and are the bases for relating quality to basic research and to agency mission. In many cases the work of a government laboratory has bearing on a large-scale research and development activity outside of government. The question of quality then becomes emphasized, and the need for basic research becomes undeniable. In defense programs, for example, it is difficult to conceive of a government laboratory which is to contribute to the common defense and which is to examine or use the work of contractors without a capability for making creative decisions and judgments leading to the advancement of the defense mission.

I could make a number of auxiliary remarks about the relation of basic research to the retention of highly qualified scientific personnel, but I believe it is sufficient to emphasize this relation and to state that it follows that basic research must be a planned-for part of the programs of all federal laboratories. For this reason, it is encouraging that policy statements of the President's Science Advisory Committee and of the National Science Foundation have noted the direct importance of basic research to government laboratories. Nothing would so damage in-house government research programs as the removal of basic research from its work. No scientist of quality would remain where the frontiers of science are closed to him.

The third point about basic research in government laboratories is somewhat elusive. Let me restate this point. Basic research in government identifies the government with an implicit responsibility of government to society. The responsibility is that of encouraging the advancement of man. I do not want to belabor this philosophical point, but I do say that government is in essence a formal organization created to improve man's condition. This may be considered a "mission" of government. Basic research is a search for understanding which helps to improve man's condition. The government, therefore, should encourage basic research in general, and it seems most appropriate that a portion of government's in-house laboratory activities should contribute to this fundamental responsibility. Is this stretching things too far?

Let me put it another way. There are important returns from basic research programs in government laboratories, returns for the laboratory personnel and for the community at large. It seems to me that government science programs must attract scientists who are dedicated to the public service. Such dedication should be closely related to the nonutilitarian values of scientific investigation.

I have been concerned that judgments about basic research have emphasized their criticality to defense, to industry, and to our standard of living. We have oversold this point and we have undersold the intellectual gift of man to examine his environment as an enhancement of his dignity. Science is, after all, concerned with knowledge and with our understanding of man in nature. This concern is inherent in what we mean by man. Must we continue to exaggerate in utilitarian terms an activity which we are compelled to support by our very natures? Should we not begin to identify our basic research activities with their very reason for being?

Obstacles to Basic Research

I want to talk now briefly about some of the obstacles to basic research in government laboratories. Here I will be leaving the realm of philosophy and entering the practical areas of money and regulations. I should like to preface these remarks by quoting from the April 1955 report by the subcommittee on research activities of the Commission on the Organization of the Executive Branch of the Government. Referring to basic research the report says, "Very little is performed in the laboratories of the Department of Defense. Since there is, in general, an inadequate environment and competence for basic research in its laboratories, the placing of substantially all of this work in the laboratories of the civilian economy is necessary." A situation which leads to such a conclusion is most unfortunate, particularly in view of the important responsibilities of these laboratories. What now are some of these factors which impede the maintenance of a suitable research environment in government laboratories?

The elements affecting the quality of the research environment in government laboratories are for the most part similar to those in any other research laboratory. But the procedural requirements within government are such that we have unusual problems in achieving optimum conditions. There is too little appreciation by the public of these problems and too little demand by a knowledgeable public for improvement in the laboratories which belong to them.

Deterrents to Scientific Personnel

The first problem is the matter of mission. Each laboratory should have a clearly defined mission. The mission should be sharp enough to provide focus, purpose, and essential elements of uniqueness yet broad enough not only to permit but to encourage creative research. In this connection, there is also the matter of laboratory direction. Research directors should be capable not only of providing inspirational leadership but they also must be given authority to match their responsibilities. In addition, there should be opportunity and incentive to remain in responsible charge long enough to see long-term research projects bear fruit and to be held accountable if the leadership errs too often.

Next we come to the man who does the research, the working scientist to whom I referred earlier as an abused resource. I am becoming more and more convinced that government personnel policies regarding scientists, in fact, regarding any specialized personnel, are unrealistic. The rules of the civil service were not made for flexibility. Furthermore, administrative procedures devised in particular agencies frequently add significantly to this inflexibility. Civil service rules were rightfully established to protect public servants from political abuse, but they do, in turn, frequently abuse specialized personnel. They often require of public servants who are scientists that they

155

make unusual financial sacrifices so that they may retain the privilege of public service. They ask them to submit to an outmoded scheme of position classification and procedure wherein positions are classified with virtually no means for recognizing the creative capabilities of specific individuals. Nor does the administrator of scientific activities have it easier. He is hampered by procedural rigidity. He cannot exercise any significant quality judgment in relation to research personnel. Under present civil service regulations the government is generally unable to offer any more, in terms of starting salary, to the top man of a graduating class than to the bottom man. There are too few opportunities to use premiums for quality. And I remind you that "quality" is the essence of good research.

Next we come to the area of equipment and facilities. Here we are dealing with a major fiscal problem. We have to achieve a greater understanding among administrators and legislators of the continuous changes of modern scientific investigations. The obsolescence of equipment must become a regular part of our planning. I am frequently faced with the problem of explaining the continuous need for new equipment, and I find great difficulty in communicating this need because almost no other area of human activity has ever been faced with such a regular dynamic condition.

A number of other problems I shall merely list in order to bring them to your attention, but I shall not discuss them. There is the problem of inadequate salaries for the top people in government labs. There is the need for providing a better mechanism which will allow scientists to escape from the trap of becoming administrators. There is the need for allowing basic research to remain free of organizational strictures. For example, regular working hours are not always compatible with research investigation. There is need for the special orientation of non-scientific personnel attached to laboratories where a substantial amount of basic research is undertaken. Within the framework of government it is very easy for the fiscal, legal, supply, and personnel experts to assume control rather than support functions. These are but a few of the important problems which must be met with vigor and wisdom if the government laboratories are to fulfill their essential role in our scientific and technological society.

Conclusions

I will end by repeating these points I made earlier: (1) Increase the federal funds available for basic research. (2) Increase the amount of basic research in government laboratories. (3) Recognize that basic research and those who conduct it are important to the whole activity of a government scientific laboratory and treat them accordingly. (4) Recognize that government has a responsibility for fostering basic research, even for its nonutilitarian values.

Basic Research in INDUSTRIAL LABORATORIES

JAMES B. FISK
Bell Telephone Laboratories

THE MATERIAL well-being of a nation and its military strength rest largely and increasingly on the technical developments exploited by its industry. Basic research, the search for new fact and understanding, has provided and continues to extend and strengthen the foundations on which technical advance and new development are built.

These statements are increasingly accepted as axioms of our society. It is hard to find examples of industrial products or services that do not owe some debt, in many instances their very existence, to basic research. If these are accepted truths, if every industrial company has some stake in basic research as a source of development opportunity, of economic growth and financial reward, why are there relatively so few who do basic research themselves or who provide funds for its support other than indirectly through the taxes they pay? In particular, why are there so few who do basic research themselves?

I think the main reasons are these: Top management may be unaware of the present needs of its technology for basic research and unaware of future values to be had from its successful conduct. Some companies will have sponsored only the immediate and urgent applied research, not seeing either the immediate or longer-term returns from basic research. And some, who have made the attempt, may have failed in providing the necessary conditions.

Values

What can industry expect? What are the values of basic research carried out in industrial laboratories? There are many. Some are direct and tangible, others intangible. Taken together, "Basic research is more practical than you think."

The first and most obvious value is new scientific knowledge of direct relevance and importance in the company's field of activity. Dramatic examples lie in important inventions, such as the transistor, which come directly and increasingly from basic research. A different example is furnished in the form of new understanding and innovation; for instance, by the research of mathematicians which led to so-called information theory and to basic new ways in which communication signals can be transmitted.

But breakthroughs and inventions and dramatic innovation are not all. The research which precedes presents the opportunity; the realization of its richness comes largely from the research which continues. The steady search for new understanding—illuminated as it will be from time to time by a brilliant event—is a true source of vigorous and dynamic technology.

The body of knowledge relevant to almost every field of technology has grown enormously, particularly in the past two decades. The rate of growth is not decreasing. The technical choices before management are correspondingly great, often subtle, and usually important. A basic research organization, competent to appraise technical potentials, can be of great value to management in its look ahead.

The interaction of research workers with development engineers in industrial laboratories is important to development, both in direct consultation and in longer-term, continuing education, and such communication can be important to the research man too. His role in this interaction is to "keep the thinking straight," to reduce empiricism, and to infuse development activity with scientific method. The quality and tone of a development organization are importantly influenced by the presence of a good basic research activity in the industrial laboratory. The research group can also be a source of excellent development engineers at the proper stage in individual careers, as experience has shown.

No industry, no industrial laboratory, can be expected to be entirely self-sufficient in generating all its technology, let alone the science on which its technology rests. To draw effectively from the broad world of science you must be a part of science, and your ticket of admission, so to speak, is your own established competence in some area of science. Then, regardless of where the discovery that is in your field of interest may be made, you will be in a position to recognize and understand, to appraise and use. You will have something to give in return. It may be simply scientific understanding and a useful exchange of ideas. It may be that the discoverer or inventor is interested in using your own discoveries and inventions. An industrial laboratory with strong basic scientists, generating much of its own new science and technology, will contribute to science, will be alert to the results of others—and will have valuable assets for exchange and use.

Essential Ingredients and Conditions

Several years ago, in a thoughtful article entitled "Vitality of a Research Institution and How to Maintain It" Ralph Bown discussed essential ingredients for successful research in an industrial laboratory. More recently Mervin Kelly, in several addresses, and, indeed, a number of participants in this symposium have spoken and written on this subject.

I expect we would all be pretty well agreed on essential conditions. If there are differences, they are likely to show up in discussion of how certain conditions are best achieved or how closely they can be approximated, or in questions of emphasis and relative importance.

Sometimes an analogy is helpful—and I have looked for one, but not very successfully. The arch is an old favorite. I can identify the keystone, the larger and some of the smaller blocks, and perhaps the mortar. But this analogy is static. Research is alive and dynamic. Perhaps it is better to assemble some of the essential ingredients and simply remember that in any complex, dynamic organism there are many of these, and many conditions to be met. Some are more important than others, but health and vigor depend on attention to all of them.

The principal ingredients for successful research in an industrial laboratory are: people, purpose, and environment.

People obviously come first: professional competence, scientists of the highest intellectual quality. This means painstaking search and careful selection of those rare individuals who have the gift of uninhibited insight so essential to research in its creative aspects. It means recognition of the role of technology in a dynamic industry, the role of science as its source, and most importantly, the role of the individual as the producer of new science. It also means generating and maintaining esprit de corps, a will to accomplishment, and a pride in accomplishment. Successful solution of these human problems determines the vitality and conditions the technical performance of a research organization.

Second is purpose. A prime need of an industrial laboratory is a clear understanding of why it exists. What are its technical and scientific objectives? "What business is it in?" so to speak. And what business does it intend to be in?

This concept, the conscious setting of objective, does no violence to basic research. It simply implies that the research man will understand the purpose of the organization, know what is technically feasible in the business, and have a criterion of relevance for his work. Because his research is relevant to the main aims of the overall organization, it need be no less basic and no less a contribution to science, as experience has frequently shown.

It is true, for example, that a laboratory devoted to improvement and extension of electrical communications is an unlikely source of new knowledge in high-energy particle physics. The reverse is also true. In both cases, however, there is enormous scope and challenge to initiative.

Beyond people and purpose there is an array of ingredients which, taken all together, make up what we will call environment—the intellectual, organizational, and economic environment in which research is carried out, and the services and facilities which support it.

Important elements of a research environment are certain freedoms.

Freedom in the choice of problems—subject to the criterion of relevance.

Freedom to carry a study to the point of demonstrating the merit of an idea—and freedom to drop the study there and go after the next good idea.

These are important freedoms for the research organization, but they are not inherent, natural rights of individuals. They are to be earned over a period of time by distinguished performance. Also, they include being able to enlist one's associates in attacking particularly challenging problems, if the problems have sufficient merit. And they will be tempered occasionally by an associate's need for help in getting over a particularly difficult hurdle.

Freedom of publication and encouragement of sound and timely publication, these, too, are important to the research environment and can be achieved in industry. Most scientists today understand the need for prompt patent applications, and a well-organized laboratory can get such work done expeditiously. Hence, patent questions need cause little delay in publication. But in any event secrecy is unattractive in basic research —and is very seldom necessary. The communication of knowledge is a responsibility of scientists, a most important mechanism of scientific advance. Any research institution which draws value from the work of others through their publications has in some degree an obligation to return value in kind. The extent to which a laboratory does so will weigh heavily in the appraisal which scientists make of it as a place to work.

Equilibrium with the scientific community is attained in part by publication. However, more than publication is necessary. The testing of one's ideas and results, and learning those of others, by direct professional association in the community of scientists is much to be encouraged. This is not primarily a matter of professional prestige; it is importantly a part of the continuing process of education, of intellectual stimulus and preparation for the research problems that lie in the future. It is a kind of "preventive maintenance," if you like, and it takes many forms, among them, scientific meetings and symposia, short or long visits to industrial laboratories by lecturers and consultants, occasionally a "sabbatical" term, in reverse, for a period of teaching and study in a university.

Basic research should be organizationally autonomous. It should not be confused with or subservient to development, or it will not survive. This does not mean that research requires a special and remote tower, on the contrary. Research, development, and development planning all have much to gain from close physical proximity, but one may not be responsible to the other if each is to do its very special and demanding work.

It is sometimes said that formal organization and research are not compatible. I do not agree with this. Orderliness in relations among people, smoothness in function, and a free flow if ideas within a conceptual framework are helped, not hindered, by a charting of function and responsibility. But the organization chart must not become master, and organizational position must not be confused with scientific stature.

A contributing scientist should be made to feel no need for organizational tail feathers in order to attain personal satisfaction and financial reward commensurate with his contribution. Within an industrial laboratory every effort must be made to insure that salary bears a direct relationship to performance, and that the compensation of professional scientists is competitive with other related opportunities. But salary alone, however important and honorable and desirable, cannot be made to substitute for long for other factors which, in sum, constitute a good research environment.

With respect to size, it is sometimes argued that if a research and development organization is large, certain psychological factors tend greatly to diminish its effectiveness. It is alleged, for example, that large groups overdo engineering and research in particular lines: that they become organizationally rigid; that they create large, deep ruts; and that they lack the flexibility to keep up with the latest discoveries in outside organizations. In a broad sense, diseases of this sort can appear in any large organization, whether or not it is devoted to research, and they are the subject of considerable concern among contemporary thinkers.

The cure, at least for research and development organizations, lies not in keeping the organization small, but in the administrative recognition of the actual nature of research. It involves appreciation of the fact that basic new scientific ideas come from individual scientists and not from "manpower," and that the research laboratory must therefore have the individual scientists clearly in focus. This is fundamentally an easy policy to administer.

Once the basic administrative policy is set, the large laboratory can be every bit as stimulating, perhaps more stimulating to research men than a small one. There are two factors which work in this direction. One is that specialists in individual areas need a certain number of immediate associates in their own fields to keep them professionally sharp and to provide natural teammates with whom to attack difficult problems. The other and perhaps more important factor is that scientific creativity tends to flourish particularly in the presence of a judicious mixture of disciplines. The brilliant individual then has people to talk to in different or neighboring fields who are just as bright as he is, and such interactions are likely to be especially fruitful in generating really new ideas.

As an example, two of the most basic advances in metallurgy in recent years, the discovery of metal "whiskers" as single crystals with strength of ten or more times that of the bulk material, and the actual visual identification and discovery of dislocation structures, were both made in the Bell Laboratories through the interaction of metallurgists with scientists in other fields. Another example, namely information theory or "cybernetics," mentioned earlier, resulted from the interaction of mathematicians and engineers.

All these observations bear on environment. The list is not complete. It should include some comments on laboratory housing and facilities, on libraries, on scientific apparatus, on the importance of adequate technical assistants, and on services and how they can be handled with minimum diversion of the research man's effort. They are all important and I believe they are quite well understood.

I will close by joining with Mervin Kelly in these thoughts: I am confident that basic research in industry will be highly productive and rewarding to the company that builds its research organization with attention to the points we have discussed. I hope that an increasing number will do so—in balance with their development effort and in keeping with the nature of their business—for it will be not only in their self-interest but also will add greatly to the nation's strength.

Basic Research in PRIVATE RESEARCH INSTITUTES

MERLE A. TUVE
Carnegie Institution of Washington

I BELIEVE that most of us accepted the invitation to participate in this symposium because we found ourselves rather largely in agreement with Dr. Weaver's provocative statement in calling for these discussions. Regardless of the doubling and redoubling year by year of the announced annual expenditures by government and industry for basic research in science, we all feel a bit helpless and disappointed because these large sums seem to contribute so little to the really basic core of scholarly accomplishment which is central to all the varied degrees and qualities of activity we now seem to include under the term basic research.

I liked particularly Dr. Weaver's third paragraph and one or two of his questions and comments:

> Strong evidence has been accumulating that we are in fact capable of creating new knowledge. But in spite of our verbal dedication to the importance of basic research, and in spite of our emerging confidence that we have the national resources of imaginative, competent, and dedicated individuals to carry out

169

basic research, it nevertheless remains true that as a nation, we are not giving adequate and suitable support to basic research.

He questions whether the applied research and massive development activities initiated and supported by government and by industry have been damaging to our activities in basic research, and whether funds for basic research are made available with "the flexibility, stability and freedom from intellectually dishonest commitment with which competent scholarship should be supported."

I was particularly unhappy to find myself giving a more than halfway affirmative answer to his question four:

> Are not universities so deeply invaded by the demands for solving immediate problems and by the temptation of income for so doing that there are all too few cases of competent scholars pondering about problems simply because it interests them to do so? Is there not a real danger that the scholars in our universities will lose—and indeed have already partly lost—the "maneuvering room for their continuing reanalysis of the universe?"

We are grateful for the invitation "to examine with candor . . . and inquire realistically what are the blocks which prevent our doing what we all say we believe is important. . . ."

Importance of the Individual Researcher

This is a fine challenge, and I doubt that we have yet fully measured up to the incisiveness of the invitation. I am still troubled by the general consent we seem to yield for the inclusion of a huge array of very expensive subsidiary or peripheral items of activity and expenditure on the same level and in the same fiscal totals with the one single item we all know to be central to the entire question, namely, the nurture and support and encouragement and protection of the creative individual investigator. The competent, interested, dedicated, lively individual investigator who participates directly and personally

in the joys and frustrations of research, who works with the research materials himself, and makes the hard choices of what
effort to abandon and what to continue is at the real center of
this problem. Suitable provision for his recruitment and his
welfare and increase in his number is unquestionably of much
greater importance than the provision of spectacular facilities
carefully calculated in tons and dollars by the businessmen and
politicians of science surely to outdo the Russians in the same
field.

Huge new synchrotrons and cosmotrons and electronic
computers, and polar expeditions and balloon and rocket flights
and great government laboratories costing more each year than
the total academic costs of many of our greatest universities—
all these conspicuous aspects of our new national devotion to
science are subsidiary and peripheral. They do not serve appreciably to produce or develop creative thinkers and productive
investigators. At best they serve them, often in a brief or a rather
incidental way, and at worst they devour them.

There is a growing conviction among my friends in academic circles that the university is no place for a scholar in
science today, because a professor's life nowadays is a rat race
of busyness and activity, managing contracts and projects,
guiding teams of assistants, and bossing crews of technicians,
plus the distractions of numerous trips and committees for
government agencies, necessary to keep the whole frenetic
business from collapse.

This picture is ignored and even denied by some, but it is
much too genuine for a great many of our academic leaders
today. Too many of our academic leaders, of course, have
chosen this pattern of activity and personal power in preference
to the quieter and more difficult life of dealing with ideas and
scholarly initiative.

In this busy and expansive world of scientific research,

new style, the private research institutes set up some decades ago do not count for much in terms of size, as measured either by numbers of workers or by yearly expenditures. The chief examples are the Rockefeller, Carnegie, Guggenheim and Bamberger establishments, and probably their greatest contributions to scientific research today are as stable and continuing prototypes of well-tested procedures for the selection and encouragement of creative individuals and the maintenance of a productive situation and environment for the scientific investigator.

We all know what we mean by truly basic research. We mean a devoted and almost passionate activity in search of new knowledge, not just factual information, but knowledge of the kind which can enlarge our *understanding*, knowledge which is not isolated facts but related to guiding hypotheses or principles, knowledge which relates to natural law. This kind of truly basic research is a creative activity, an expression of wonder and the love of knowledge, and it is correspondingly a highly personal activity. It is concerned with ideas, hopefully and critically directed toward understanding, and it is often the spontaneous effort of one man, or at most of several competent individuals working together. It is not directed or organized, and only in the later stages, often close to technology or to medical use, does it lead to the employment of large groups of specialists operated as a team. By contrast, then, it is the support of ideas by the support of the individual research man who has ideas.

I believe the private institutions which operate today to carry forward this well-recognized kind of basic research have as their most important function simply the preservation of a prototype of this kind. Their activities comprise well-tested arrangements for the increase of knowledge and understanding, and they are based on the subsidy of fundamental research by the support of selected individuals who work directly with the materials of their ideas. This kind of operation is a way of life together for a small group of dedicated investigators. It is a quest, not a job to be done. The measure of their success is the quality of their efforts and the character of their critical selection of goals to be sought, not the quantity of their output of scientific results. These men serve the conviction that greater knowledge and deeper understanding are undeniably good.

Continued support of this conviction by the maintenance of prototype activities is then, I think, the principal service to basic research which is now to be asked and expected of the private research institutes, or at least of those private agencies which were established many years ago, when there was less financial and technical exuberance, with regard to the support and administration of research effort, than we see all about us today.

Confusion between Scientific and Technological Activities

We have lumped under "Research and Development" so many huge technological activities in the national budget, and correspondingly in corporation budgets and elsewhere, that the figures have become practically meaningless. Under "Research" and even under "Basic Research" we have encouraged and budgeted huge enterprises of essentially operational character, most of them promoted with some enthusiastic hope of great national prestige. Essentially these projects are based on the twin arguments that the United States must be first and biggest, and that tax money is not real money but just a voucher for directing the expenditure of national effort toward certain speculative goals because otherwise this effort would not be spent at all or would just be directed toward more personal goals.

After the special usefulness in war technology of men

trained in basic physical sciences had been demonstrated during World War II, the idea of *mission-directed basic research* was firmly implanted by our concerted efforts at numerous locations in the dark recesses of the military budgets. We have all been faithfully supervising the growth of this hybrid notion ever since, in the halls of Congress and in the minds of the public. We all know that only an extremely small fraction of the various budgets we help to defend are for truly basic research in the sense of intensive studies devoted to the perception and formulation of new knowledge toward deeper understanding.

Basic research was enlarged long ago to include the personal accumulation of information known to be of little or no present interest to others. But first the engineers and chemists, and then all of us, began to include under "Basic Research" the systematic accumulation of measurements by organized groups of technicians with a view to the usefulness of the resulting tables of data for various technological purposes. This kind of activity by large groups of technicians has expanded far beyond systematic data-taking to include whole experimental programs on a speculative basis, only very thinly flavored with the personal interest of a competent individual and containing only minute traces of the love of knowledge. The use of large groups of technicians had enlarged the budgets and the support of research long before World War II. We all embraced this precedent heartily when the opportunity for much larger postwar funds appeared, and we excused ourselves by saying that even five per cent of these new big sums would underwrite larger opportunities than were ever previously available for studying the basic problems which really interested us.

I might give a mild example. I have served for many years on the Executive Committee of the United States National Committee for the International Geophysical Year. When the Russians announced that they would join this cooperative world activity, the IGY became important as an example of international collaboration which could be carried on in spite of crucial differences in political policies and beliefs. The success of the IGY was important for reasons which probably transcended the intrinsic value of the detailed scientific observations themselves. As a consequence, on the Executive Committee we had to judge and approve expenditures which seemed outrageously large in relation to their possible scientific merit or importance, and we served as the excuse for logistics costs for various polar expeditions and airplane and rocket flights which cost money enough to have subsidized the physical sciences in great luxury at all our universities for many decades. All the money was spent, mostly, of necessity, by our military services. We encountered or produced in the IGY many examples of a drastic loss of a sense of proportion between the costs of a project and its substantive content.

I would like to point out that all of us have contributed to a more or less purposeful confusion in our use of the words "basic research." It seems to me that a great deal of the money listed as spent for basic research is spent for highly technological activities and operations, and that far too small a fraction of it, indeed, is actually spent for the subsidy of thinking, by giving to selected, competent individuals both the freedom and the time to think. When a scientific scholar, as distinguished perhaps from a business executive, speaks of basic research, surely he must have primary reference to the *support of ideas,* not the operations aspect of technological performances or record achievements, however spectacular, such as submarine trips under the polar ice or successful Antarctic logistics for the IGY.

I might suggest that for purposes of discussion the term "academic research" could be considered to refer to the intensely personal activity of individual professional workers in search of scientific knowledge, the kind of activity we all recognize as basic research, even during its drudgery stages, and that the term "technological research" be used to refer to the very much larger body of activity, often involving a great many individuals not qualified as independent investigators, which underlies, in its matter of fact way, the work of various practical groups in industry and government. Basic research, which is so-called mission-directed, is then primarily technological research, although an occasional activity which really does qualify under the notion of the "support of ideas" will be *mission-connected* and might even be included in the budgets for what I would call technological research. But this we all know is a very small fraction.

The reason for making this perhaps uncomfortable distinction is not in order to attack technological research as such, except on perhaps one point, namely, that it deflects, distracts, and subtracts some highly creative and effective individuals from the research area we clearly recognize as the support of ideas, into this rather special operating area of technology. The reason for making the distinction is simply to remind you of a genetic relationship, namely, that all the huge activities of technological research grow out of the highly personal activities of academic research. No array of feedback arguments will convince very many of us that the real germ of new knowledge is the product of team activity or the result of large-scale instruments or implements created in the simple hope of learning something new. The idea and the research objective must come first and then the instrument created for approaching this objective and testing the idea. Occasionally, but often in an equivocal sense, this notion that teams and big instruments create new areas of knowledge appears partly true or at least plausible. But I have observed that the new scientific knowledge gained by just operating a huge expedition or big-scale instrumentation often must be inflated by repeated public statements until it appears to have great scientific importance. When asked seriously about it, the noninvolved workers in the relevant scientific field are frequently unable to say why the results obtained should be considered so important, except that they cost a lot or involve such a spectacular effort. Most of our present hoop-la about space is certainly in this category.

Creation of Favorable Environment

What has all this to do with basic research in private research institutes? I can say it very simply. The enormous expansion of funds and activities called research has left the private research institute as only a minuscule item in the whole picture, but the function of a research institute seems thereby to have become even more clearcut and conspicuous. It must function as a stable and continuing prototype. In discussing the activities of my own department in the Carnegie Institution I have said for some years that it is very simply our aim "to be just a good old-fashioned example of the real thing." By this, of course, we mean that we attempt to support the highly personal activity of the individual research man who does his own research work. This is our interpretation of the "support of ideas." The support of thinking, in the search for new knowledge, is always the support of a man. No newer idea, no team concept, and no devotion to huge facilities can take the place of this old requirement and this traditional precept.

This basic idea of Mr. Carnegie and his advisors, of buying a man's time and giving it back to him, as a support for his ideas and his thinking, has some important corollary aspects. One is that he must not have too many people interfering with his time or he becomes a manager and an operator more than a research man. Another corollary is, especially in these days, that his equipment will be smaller and less complicated than the best equipment in his field of work, or again he will be converted into a manager or a constructor or a big time operator.

In general the corollary is simply one of *reasonable austerity*. Many of us who have soberly discussed the environment required to foster creative personal activity recognize that a moderate degree of austerity is essential to the hard work and disciplined self-criticism which are always required for creative intellectual accomplishment.

Austerity as an essential requirement for creative research may sound harsh and out of date to most of the big operators and many of the young technical men in research today. For these discussions, however, I wish you would recall to yourselves some of the examples of finished basic research which you most honestly respect and then answer the austerity question silently for yourself. This meeting is supposed to attempt some candidly honest evaluations. It is not a budget hearing but more nearly a study of principles. The undeniable fact is that creative work is almost always done with limited resources and under difficult conditions. I suggest that this austerity is to a considerable extent a necessary discipline for the critical faculty and a basis for the Spartan choices which must be made by the investigator as to emphasis and deletion in the course of any basic research.

Nearly all the half dozen privately supported research institutes which are known to me give direct allegiance to the idea of supporting basic research by supporting individual investigators who do much of the work themselves. It is well known that the Rockefeller and Carnegie research institutes and the Institute for Advanced Study take this position.

The Guggenheim Foundation, in its way, is an operating agency exhibiting perhaps the purest form of support of basic research by the support of individual investigators. Some of the newer agencies, it is true, have used their private resources in greater or lesser measure as a backstop and a basis for utilizing government grants and other temporary public funds. The Bartol Foundation has enlarged its activities considerably on this basis, I understand, and the Sloan-Kettering Institute is a conspicuous example.

Whether an operation very greatly expanded beyond the capabilities of its private funds by the acceptance of short-term grants and contracts is correspondingly more fruitful in really basic research, correspondingly more productive of new and genuine scientific knowledge, as distinguished from technological investigations, I believe is still undetermined. It is true that those who actually carry forward the various research programs supported by these discontinuous grants for projects would be vastly more free in their efforts and less concerned with how their work may look to others if they were operating entirely on continuing private funds, as under endowments.

In addition, numerous smaller private research funds, which I shall not attempt to enumerate, especially those related to research professorships or to individual departments, as in some medical schools, fit rather well with our criteria of supporting basic research by supporting a selected man, and of operating under at least a moderate degree of austerity.

It is important for us to recognize the relatively small size of the annual budget for this academic kind of basic research. The overall total probably does not reach twice what it was before the war in terms of a constant dollar. Even though our methods are more wasteful, and we buy numerous industrial tools and instruments, and we pay all of our graduate students, the total number of competent and fully trained investigators who are really devoted to seeking new laws and new regularities in nature's processes and are not guided toward practical ends such as better radio or radar or better submarine detection or navigation or better rockets or antibiotics is not large. The number of these academic men in basic research is still not too different from the prewar number of similar fully trained scientific investigators. In some ways we must take a larger discount, because so many of our principal research men now spend such a large fraction of their time in obtaining and spending large government grants and in supervising large groups of rather poorly qualified workers who have been upgraded into posts as research men but who are not qualified to be independent investigators. It is my impression that the total effort really spent on basic scientific research in the old-fashioned or scholarly sense has not increased by more than a modest fraction and in no way can be compared with the huge figures of five hundred million and eight hundred million dollars per year which are supposed to be spent for basic research in this country.

How much basic research do we "need"? Why do we think we should have more basic research? I have not been able to recognize any objective basis for making a quantitative statement about our need for basic research as I have described it. Even a relative statement regarding quantity, such as the remark that we need much more basic research than we have in progress today, is hardly to be demonstrated objectively. But we each have our convictions on the subject, and I suggest that we should recognize the depth and quality of our convictions, and note that they actually rest on a higher and broader foundation than, for example, can be objectively demonstrated by economic statistics or by the calculable limitations of our present-day technology. I do not agree that the primary reason for underwriting basic research in science is a utilitarian one, to provide new facts and ideas to be utilized by industry. Instead, one of the good reasons for us to have a productive industrial plant is to give us some excess social energy to invest in science and the arts for their own sakes. Our individual convictions regarding academic research are thus rooted in our views of what constitutes the good life. We all feel that a prosperous society should not spend its entire energy and resources in enjoyments of the moment, but that it should also add some permanent enrichment to the lives of others (and, for that matter, to the lives of its own individuals). Higher education is recognized in the United States as in itself a "higher good." Scholarly achievement, the recognition and delineation of new knowledge, is nearly everywhere in our country granted a position of respect and honor.

The real foundation, then, for an examination of the question as to how much of this kind of genuine basic research we need does not lie in our predictions as to the needs of industry or technology for more facts and for new areas of industrial activity or profitable investment. Nor does it lie in the continuingly imminent sterility of our efforts to resolve the differences between the value system of our society and those of other societies by a sheer increase in our ability to destroy or to use force.

The problem of the quantity of basic research needed in our present society, academic research, as distinguished from applied research or mission-directed research, thus rests on our joint estimate of two things: (a) how high in our value system do we place scholarly achievement, or the creative search for new ideas and the formulation of new knowledge, and (b) how much of our national effort can we now afford to invest in these fruits of our prosperity and our convictions?

Each of us has his own rough answers to these two questions, but I have great confidence that most of our public servants, including industrialists and newspaper columnists along with our elected representatives at all levels, have overestimated our willingness to underwrite our fears and have underestimated our willingness to underwrite our hopes. The position of education, and especially of higher education, in the value scale of the adult American, the working taxpayer, is still well up toward the top of the list.

Even though our present level of effort in academic research in science is reasonably high—in part because graduate students are young and idealistic and there are many of them because the available project money pays each one a good stipend—it could be higher. The quality of the effort could represent a deeper commitment to the search for truth and beauty if we seriously undertook to devise and support measures which are honestly directed toward the best support of individual creativeness in science. There is much of it in every fresh generation of graduate students, but I feel that we have directed most of our efforts toward the creation and support of large-scale activities essentially technological in character and conspicuous in possible effects. We have not had much success, as a nation, in encouraging quietly creative scholarship and intensely personal activity in research. Our state universities and our larger private institutions did this moderately well but on a modest scale twenty and thirty years ago, but this kind of local enthusiasm seems less prevalent now that large grants, by every scale of comparison, are made to individual professors. And these professors are selected for support not by faculties and deans or faculty research committees who know them, but by their own self-esteem (that is, by their personal requests for support) and by boards or panels in Washington. It is at least highly probable that the present system of selection for research support, strongly biased in favor of the excessively self-confident person and the "big operator," is not well designed to favor the quietly creative scholar. Perhaps all we need is the noisily creative scholar, but he is surely a bit less genuinely decorative to our society, and his contributions, although suitably expensive, are probably less permanently valuable.

Proposed Method of Operation

I now turn with some hesitation to the suggestion of a mechanism which might serve to increase and stabilize the level of creative basic research in our country. My hesitation relates only to the question of using federal funds in our educational institutions, but perhaps this has already been accepted by most of you. In any case, I believe we should take firm position on the point that the support of true basic research is the support of ideas, and this always means the support of a creative investigator. I think we should make it clear to Congress and to the public that the whole basic record of scientific progress has been made by individual men who could spend their time freely on the scientific problems which puzzled them. I see no valid reason for not insisting that the sound support of basic research requires us to use the technique long used in the universities and copied by the private research institutes, namely, that of buying a creative man's time and giving it back to him. Endowment has been the technique previously used, by the ancient universities and by the Carnegies and Rockefellers and others. Congress may have strong views against granting public funds as permanent endowment, but we can surely insist that there are specific and identifiable individuals in the world of scientific research whose lifetime efforts can safely be underwritten in advance as good single investments in basic research.

I mean thus to say that we might use public funds to purchase a creative investigator's working lifetime, and then give it back to him to spend in his research efforts. A single lump sum of say $700,000 would pay the remaining lifetime salary of a gifted research man after he has been clearly identified as a creative investigator by the age of 30 or 35, and would pay in addition for one or two technical assistants or two or three students to work with him. We could stipulate to the Regents or Trustees who accepted such a lump sum to underwrite the scientific investigator's lifetime activities that if he changed from the life of a working research scholar to become a manager of large grants or the supervisor of a large team, the Regents would shift him to their own salary rolls and revert the grant which made him a Distinguished Research Scholar.

One might call such an investigator a Franklin Research Professor or a Jefferson Research Scholar. If we were to allocate 40 to 60 million dollars per year to the creation of such Research Professors or Research Scholars, suitably selected by a very small University Grants Committee, in one decade we would have in this country a solid phalanx of 500 or 600 outstanding investigators dedicated to basic research and unquestionably free to devote their personal time and attention to creative ideas for the rest of their lives. The total investment over a decade of 400 to 600 million dollars would amount to perhaps half the cost of one year of our current activity with space rockets or perhaps the cost of operating the U. S. Atomic Energy Commission for two months.

You are all asked at regular intervals to consider and support programs in individual specialties such as nuclear physics or oceanography or space rocketry or meteorology or the chemotherapy of cancer with sums of public money each totaling from 50 to 800 million dollars per year. If we all believe that the real key to basic research is the continued stable support of the individual research man, to give him full freedom, with moderate austerity, to investigate problems in which he is interested, then "What are the blocks which prevent our doing what we all say we believe is important?"

Support of
Basic Research
from GOVERNMENT

PAUL E. KLOPSTEG
National Science Foundation

THE PRECEDING papers have dealt most skillfully with the central theme of this symposium, with the many points of view from which the speakers and panels have clarified the subject. Nonetheless, in dealing with basic research in a particular setting, it is still not easy to establish and preserve clarity in an unavoidably blurred image, the image created by the much abused, not to say tortured word research.

Basic Research Defined

There are many definitions of basic research. If one were to compile those which have been published, they would fill many pages. This has been done, and they do. When designed to enlighten the layman, including the members of the Congress, or to set boundaries for esoteric discussions, they invariably deal with the researcher's attitudes and motives. They are primarily descriptive. Curiosity, desire for new knowledge, urge to expand horizons, interest in a problem, the excitement of being first in unexplored territory, absence of concern over pragmatic implications—one or more of these ideas always appear in some form in the definitions of basic research. Further requirements may be set to stamp the activity as basic. One is freedom for the investigator from commitments to reach specified goals. Another is freedom of publication solely at the scientist's discretion.

Within the past decade it has become accepted practice to provide federal money for research in annually increasing amounts. To allocate the funds wisely necessitates not only recognition and understanding of the kind of research to be supported, but, to serve as a future guide, a *post hoc* record of obligations or expenditures. The National Science Foundation in its task of collecting such data from the various government departments and agencies and of analyzing and presenting them annually in its publication, *Federal Funds for Science*, adopted the following "working" definition to identify projects as basic research:

> Basic research is that type of research which is directed towards increase of knowledge in science. It is research where the primary aim of the investigator is a fuller knowledge or understanding of the subject under study, rather than a practical application thereof.

Even a working definition cannot avoid descriptive aspects. This one was designed to be hopefully submitted to the agencies having to do with basic research, so that they might produce cogent, comparable fiscal data, comparable both in successive years in a given agency and among different agencies. The data are supplied mainly by fiscal officers with some guidance, one may hope, from science administrators. Wide variation in the interpretations of the working definition are inevitable. Since the intent of the investigator is involved—a matter not usually disclosed by the accounting records—this requires an unaccustomed effort by the fiscal officer to appraise motives. One may further suppose, in observing the budgetary procedures from year to year, that those having the task of assessing the motives of investigators may themselves be moved by considerations other than to provide objective information about government money obligated for basic research.

Questions of expediency may affect the reporting of data, not only in government but also in the universities, which are the principal and proper beneficiaries of funds for basic research. In the data for one particular year, universities reported about twice the amount indicated by the government agencies as having been allotted to universities for basic research. It may be that universities want the record to show that their research is truly basic, and that agencies want to emphasize their "practical" approach. Such differences cast doubt on the reliability of figures. However, the National Science Foundation is striving to obtain an increasingly dependable picture of government support of science.

Parenthetically, we probably agree that dollars are not the most suitable measure for either quantity or quality of research. In a particular field, where its needs for apparatus and equipment are stabilized in some pattern, the numbers which express cost make possible some internal appraisals and comparisons. Among fields where differences in method and needs for facilities are wide, such comparisons must have fairly low significance. More significant would be man-days or man-months applied to research by competent scientists.

Having laid a foundation of uncertainty, let me make a few observations to aid in drawing our thinking together. In doing this I have in mind a concept rather than a definition of basic research. It is what a member of a university faculty would do to advance scholarship in his field of learning if he had complete freedom of action, with needed financing. The concept is consistent with the conviction that basic research and higher education are inseparable; indeed, that basic research is essential to maintaining the highest level in higher education.

187

1. Any government administrator with experience in his field of science and broad acquaintance among those engaged in basic research can carry on his duties without having to depend on a formal definition.

2. Although our topic is government support, i.e., funding of external research, the basic research done by government agencies in their own laboratories is also, and obviously, government supported. The fraction of departmental funds devoted to internal basic research is relatively small.

3. Very few industrial corporations engaged in research, development, and engineering conduct basic research, and among those that do, the work is related to the interests of the company, and constitutes a relatively small fraction of the total activity. Government support is seldom, if ever, involved.

4. So-called research foundations with laboratories and technical staff do little basic research. Their purpose is primarily to make technical studies and developments for clients. They perform an important function, and some of them do excellent work for the government under contract. More government contract work might well be done by nonprofit foundations and corporations, and correspondingly less by universities.

5. The pattern of government support for basic research which requires large facilities and equipment and research teams beyond the most imaginative predictions of two decades ago has been firmly established. Such work, usually conducted in government-owned laboratories, has become a highly significant and indispensable part of our national effort in basic research. Its scope and scale are sure to increase. More such laboratories and institutes, operated by a university or an association of universities, will be established. Under construction, for example, are the National Radio Astronomy Observatory at Green Bank, and the stellar and solar optical observatories at Kitt Peak. Plans for a National Institute for Atmospheric Research are

well advanced. A major effort in oceanographic research will be government-supported. Reseach undertakings of the magnitude illustrated are beyond the capability of any university to support out of its own funds.

6. The government has also assumed responsibility for financing some kinds of major projects at individual universities, where reactors, accelerators, and computers, and, in the biological field, controlled environment facilities are essential. The importance of such research is beyond question, and it is possible of accomplishment only with government support.

7. There remains a very substantial research potential, beyond that needed for large-scale undertakings, among capable individuals completely devoted to scholarship: members of college and university faculties, eager to do research as part of their academic activity. Some institutions traditionally use their own funds to support their scholars' research. Many scientists also receive support from government agencies, mostly on a project basis. Notwithstanding the well-deserved reputation for careful and honest administration enjoyed by these agencies, the recipients of their support must be subjected to at least a minimum of control, since public funds are involved.

8. Our institutions of higher learning are the traditional and certainly the principal instrumentality through which new knowledge is created by the scholarly work of their faculties. This is doubly significant, for on the same institutions rests also the responsibility for identifying and training brilliant young minds, and encouraging and developing their creativity. Creation of new knowledge and the production of new creators of new knowledge at the maximum feasible rate are essential to the nation's economic, social, and physical health.

9. The Congress is appropriating many millions of dollars annually for supporting superior students in postgraduate work in the sciences. This is *prima facie* evidence of public recogni-

tion of direct government responsibility to train more research scientists and teachers of science. It constitutes indirect but important and effective support of research by government.

Impetus to Science Given by Government

Recent events in the higher levels of the Executive Branch of Government may be a memorable and perhaps historic step in making a permanent and important place for science and technology in the councils of government. The President's Science Advisory Committee in its report of December 28, 1958, to the President thoroughly reviewed the role of government in strengthening American science. The report deals with basic and applied research and with development. Its principal recommendation was put in effect by executive order on March 13, 1959, to establish a Federal Council for Science and Technology, with the President's Special Assistant for Science and Technology as chairman. The Council will undoubtedly find in the other recommendations of the Committee a working guide packed with problems, by which policies in science and technology will be clarified and further developed.

One of the major questions in the area of basic research is the manner of allocating appropriations to departments and agencies for intramural research and external support, principally in colleges and universities. Involved in this will be the breakdown by fields of science, and the "proper" fraction of funds for science and technology to be assigned to basic research. Other policy decisions on matters noted in the report should improve the coordination in basic research activities and support among departments and agencies. To discuss the report in detail would take far more time than can be devoted to it here.

Let us now have another look at the large facilities which were mentioned earlier. Whether they be called laboratories, institutes, field stations, or research centers, they have demonstrated their indispensability to acceleration of progress in science. Among their other advantages, they provide means not otherwise easily found for many scientists to exercise their creativity, and for university scientists to have occasional use of equipment not available in their own institutions. To the latter they also offer the intellectual stimulation of conferences and seminars attended by large, diverse groups. Such centers should be located so as to facilitate the interchange of staff members and faculty members of universities, and to give easy access to graduate students for thesis research.

Within ten years the investment of government funds in such centers devoted to basic research will probably be of the order of a billion dollars, and government-financed facilities within universities will represent an investment of perhaps $400 million, with operating costs in both cases at an annual figure of about 25 per cent of capital costs.

The major responsibility for large efforts in basic research with respect both to capital investment and operating costs has undergone a shift from the universities to the government. The reason is clear. Government has money, which, in part, it takes from its citizens by way of taxes. Universities have no such effective method for getting it. Finding sufficient operating funds to cover their growing needs becomes more difficult from year to year. Public attitude makes it mandatory also to give instructional budgets first claim on income, with research interests of the faculty somewhere near the end of the line. Under existing conditions, higher education can therefore hardly avoid seeking aid from government to produce and maintain superior creative scholarship and to train new scholars.

Another circumstance helps to explain the shift, namely, the change in the pattern of basic research in the university from prewar to postwar. Many more dollars, even at 1938 value, are required today to maintain a research scholar than were needed in 1938.

Prior to the war, research was regarded as a normal part of academic duties by those with a scholarly bent. There was no easing of teaching loads to make more time for research available. Spurred by his own initiative and drive, the researcher was found in his laboratory on his "free" afternoons, Sundays, holidays, and many evenings. Special apparatus was constructed either by himself or the departmental mechanic in a poorly equipped shop. The departmental budget had no line item in which the word "research" appeared. But everyone knew that the budget had in it some small though unidentified allowance for things needed for research. Research took great devotion and great effort. Yet it was fun, it was challenging, it was satisfying.

During the war years, beginning in 1940, scientists and their institutions became accustomed to doing work with military objectives under a type of contract drawn so as to defray all costs, to keep the institutions free from loss in doing the work. Before the end of the war, many colleges and universities participated in such contract work, in which many thousands of their scientists were serving their country in time of crisis, putting aside their own research to do so. When war's end came, many had had their fill of finding practical and especially military applications of science, and wanted no more secret projects behind locked doors, with results that could not be published. They were eager to resume their normal activities of basic research and teaching.

Whether for better or for worse, the outlook of many of the prewar research scientists had changed. They had become conditioned to opulence in the laboratory. They felt the need of paid assistants and clerical help as provided under the development contracts. Money had become the indispensable desideratum for their research, in amounts envisioned only in pleasant dreams before the war. The pattern for military research had become the pattern for basic research also; their productive scholarship could not come to full blossom in the old pattern. Many of the institutions also had come to regard large funds as essential to doing research. This may have been a reaction to the difficulty of reducing budgets. Even the government finds such reduction impossible. The changed attitudes, with general recognition that the prewar, leisurely pace in research no longer measured up to the postwar needs, made the shift in fiscal responsibility from universities to government inevitable. On balance, research activities have substantially grown in volume under the new conditions.

In mentioning that many institutions work assiduously to secure government contracts for specified services, no criticism is intended. Where the work fits the special aptitudes of faculty personnel, and where it contributes measurably to improvement in the performance of a department in its duties to the students, such a contract is advantageous. It is best suited for departments which normally are concerned with the more practical aspects of science, such as engineering and medicine. Such a contract, with little or no emphasis on basic research, is one kind of government support. It makes available some uncommitted money for indirect costs, the kind of money urgently needed. This can, however, become a strong inducement for institutions to seek contracts for work which they would not consider at all, were their own funds adequate to allow them complete freedom of action.

If a proposed contract for specified services were to become the responsibility of a department of basic science, questions would arise which university administrations surely would have to ask themselves. Such a department has equal status with others in the liberal arts group in advancing and disseminating knowledge valued for its cultural aspects. Would such a contract

193

introduce serious risk of lowering the scholarly excellence of the department? Could the work be done better elsewhere? Would the pressure to meet deadlines deprive a scientist of opportunity to pursue his intellectual interests, of time for undisturbed thinking? Would the work require the shifting of duties to persons of lesser experience and rank? Would additional personnel without academic status have to be hired? What future commitments might be implied? In short, would the acceptance of the contract be good for the university? Does it fall within the best array of proper university functions? Objective answers to such searching questions would in some cases undoubtedly counsel against accepting the contract.

Increasing University Funds

Since the major responsibility for basic research rests on our institutions of higher learning, it is here that the best minds and skills for work of such supreme importance should be gathered. To approach this ideal, universities must become financially able to provide the environment conducive to scholarship and to establish a salary scale which will keep scholars contented. Both could be realized with substantially increased income. How, in view of their limited resources, can the college and university hope to become the preferred habitat of the brilliant scholar? Is there no solution other than pouring in government funds?

If adequate funds are the principal answer, what is the basis for judging adequacy? The minimum needed is that which assures break-even operation to meet the demands of instruction, research, and such services to the students, the faculty, and the public as the institution regularly performs. Adequate resources, by reasonable standards, would be substantially above minimum, for improvement as needed, and for expansion to handle the oncoming rise in college population. Under ever greater population pressure, no institution can long remain complacent and rigidly limit its admissions, thus shifting responsibility for the growing load to others. If the principle is worth preserving that every capable young person should have the opportunity for higher education, each institution must assume its share of the task, for all exist to serve the public interest.

The importance of increasing general operating funds cannot easily be exaggerated, and it is properly stressed within the subject of this discussion; for higher education is the matrix within which basic research must continue to develop and flourisk. We cannot speak realistically about support for basic research without having in view the soundest possible development in both size and quality of our higher educational system. Soundness includes the moderation of seeming needs by prudent management in both the academic and administrative operations.

After a quarter century of public conditioning, the idea comes almost automatically that of course government must come to the rescue where local efforts fail for whatever reason; and, of course, the federal treasury is inexhaustible. When government pays the bill, it costs no one anything. There's no need to worry!

If the attitude should prevail of relaxedly leaning on government to solve the growing problem of keeping higher education not only solvent but vigorous, the result would surely be that more and more institutions, in trying to keep up with increasing demands, would incur deficits, and government would have to assume the annual operating loss. Moreover, this would not make them more vigorous; more likely, it would have the opposite effect. Several independent estimates indicate a prospective student population of 6½ to 7 million in 1969, and a total budget of about double what it is today. It would seem inevitable, then, that ten years hence practically every college and university would be dependent on government to cover deficit operations.

Direct government subsidy by way of general funds for higher education is most undesirable—if not, indeed, infeasible —in our situation. Consider the great diversity in kind and purpose of our institutions; consider that every one is located in a congressional district; consider the ease with which a member of the Congress can exert pressure; and consider the empire-building tendencies of bureaucracy.

If the threat of diminished autonomy is cause for apprehension, which I believe it to be, then we have a challenging and major job, easy to define but difficult to accomplish. Clearly, it is the task of recovering, preserving, and maintaining self-determination for higher education, in all its responsibilities. An effective way would be to induce such a flow of support, from large numbers of private sources, in such volume as to minimize or prevent deficits. This would minimize or obviate the need for Government subsidy and, hence, the threat of intrusion or control. The suggestion may sound too obvious or too visionary to deserve attention, but since no other alternative has appeared, it should be examined critically.

It is the millions of individuals with active or potential interest in higher education who constitute a source which will produce a much greater volume of uncommitted gifts, if a strong, positive incentive for making them can be established.

Why are such private sources not now doing what is so seriously needed? On this question, it is illuminating to consider how the operation of the internal revenue code affects the ability of an individual to make charitable gifts. Significant is the provision of permitting tax-free gifts up to 30 per cent of the donor's adjusted gross income. If all took advantage in full of this seeming magnanimity of the law, gifts based on estimated adjusted gross income for 1958 might have been upwards of $70 billion, and the government's loss of revenue about $15 billion. Government ostensibly is willing to forego many billions of income to stimulate the taxpayer's generosity. Actually, his generous impulses appear to be inhibited and revenue not jeopardized, as shown by the fact that for many years, donors itemizing gifts have given but 4 per cent of the total of adjusted

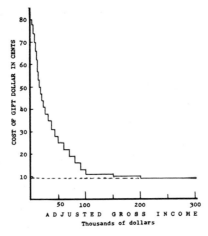

FIGURE 1. Graph based on tables accompanying income tax forms, showing cost of giving for all taxable incomes. The dotted line indicates equalization of costs, as here proposed.

gross incomes. Amendments which raised the upper limit from 15 per cent to 20 per cent, then to 30 per cent, did not affect the percentage given.

A search for possible reasons for this stability leads to an examination of the income tax provisions. In the highest income group, the cost of making a one-dollar gift is 9 cents; and for the lowest income subject to tax, the cost is 80 cents. This results from the 91 per cent and 20 per cent maximum tax rates, respectively, for the two extreme cases cited. Thus the cost of giving is nearly nine times as great for the person with the lowest taxable income as it is for his affluent friend. Simply stated, under the present tax law, the incentive for the lower-income groups to make gifts is strongly negative. On substantially over one-half of the total number of returns with adjusted gross incomes ranging between $5,000 and $50,000, deductions are itemized. In this group, and in the relatively much smaller number with higher incomes, we find the great majority of persons with more than passing interest in higher education. Their gift dollars cost them from 41 to 78 cents. In the middle-income group, the annual income is so depleted by cost of living and other obligations, including taxes, that relatively few dollars remain. Competition for them, from both within the family and outside, makes the intrinsic worth of the "surplus" dollar very great as compared with that of the tax-paid dollar of the high-income group.

Recognition of this situation suggests the desirability of an amendment to the internal revenue code, based on a principle which is equitable to the taxpayer. This principle is that the cost of giving should be no greater for those with small incomes than for those whose incomes are large. A method has been devised by which the cost of gifts for higher education is equalized for all taxpayers.

The desirability of amending the internal revenue code to accomplish such equalization of cost of giving has been expressed in various publications by individuals and groups. For example, the President's Committee on Education beyond the High School in its final report made the recommendation:

> That the Federal revenue laws be revised in ways which will even more strongly encourage larger contributions from more individuals to educational institutions. Partial credits against taxes are a way to equalize the advantage of such giving between larger and smaller incomes.

The simplest way that has been found to accomplish such equalization is the subject of a bill, H.R. 2440, to amend the internal revenue code. Its stated purpose is:

> . . . to provide funds for educational purposes by providing increased incentives for private giving through the allowance of a tax credit for charitable contributions to institutions of higher education.

The bill, introduced by Congressman Frank Thompson, Jr. of New Jersey follows recommendations growing out of a study sponsored by the American Association for the Advancement of Science to explore various ways of stimulating private giving. Enactment of the bill into law would be in accord with the government's approval of giving, and would provide a method for inducing a substantial increase in the flow of uncommitted funds to higher education. The potential benefits of the bill are so impressive that a brief summary seems appropriate.

Provisions of the amendment would be permissive, not mandatory. The taxpayer could take his contributions to higher education as a partial credit against his computed tax. The credit would be 91 per cent of such gifts up to 15 per cent of his adjusted gross income, making the cost to him 9 cents per dollar given. Based on the AAAS-sponsored study, equalization is provided also for those in lower-income groups who now use the standard deduction. They may itemize their gifts and, in addition to the standard deduction now allowed, take 91 per cent of such gifts up to 5 per cent of adjusted gross income as a credit against computed tax, thus giving them the same cost of 9 cents per dollar. Costs of donations to higher education would also be equalized among corporations by employment of tax credits for gifts up to 10 per cent of taxable income.

Should the bill become law, colleges and universities could vigorously step up their campaigns for funds, with prospects of securing very substantial increases and many new contributors.

The institutions would have a strong incentive to work harder for funds for which they would be accountable only to their own boards of direction. For the donor, the opportunity of individual decision on amounts and objects of gifts would increase his interest in higher education generally and sustain it specifically in the institutions which he helps to support.

Another substantial benefit inures to the taxpayer through direct giving. It has been estimated that for each dollar going to a university via government, the individual or corporation must pay between two and three dollars in taxes. This means that the tax dollar has one-half to two-thirds of its value worn away while in the government pipelines. Direct giving therefore means a substantial net saving to the taxpayer.

It is impossible to predict with assurance to what extent gifts to higher education would increase under the proposed amendment. In the years following its adoption, the present rate of giving might rise six, eight, perhaps ten times. Certainly the fraction of adjusted gross income given would increase very substantially. Effects of the suggested change could be learned only by trial. It is an experiment very much worth trying. To make the experiment possible, permissive legislation is needed.

If the proposed plan is thought to be less than perfect— and no plan can lay claim to perfection—its flaws must be weighed against its positive and beneficial features. If the latter heavily outweigh the former, adoption of the plan would not only provide the benefits, but also present the opportunity of making improvements prescribed by experience. Imperfections should not be a bar to adoption, but rather should offer a challenge for devising such improvements as might be desirable. A special challenge faces those who believe in the objective, namely, to assure action without further delay for stimulating and increasing private giving to higher education. If there is a better plan, it should take the place of the one proposed. The time for theorizing about the adequate financing of colleges and universities is past, and action is overdue.

Passage of the amendment, or of a better one with the same objectives, would constitute a forward-looking method of government support of the basic research which is the traditional responsibility of higher education. It would be an act difficult to match in its beneficial impact on the interest of the intelligent citizen in higher education and in its assurance of preserving the freedom and integrity of an instrumentality of incalculable worth to the nation's future.

Support of
Basic Research
by INDUSTRY

ROBERT E. WILSON*

Introduction

OTHERS HAVE already stressed some of the important aspects of the problem which the country faces in endeavoring to assure more adequate support for basic research in a period when applied research has expanded with unprecedented rapidity. Industry has rather generally been considered to be the principal villain in the picture, and not without reason. Industry has been using up the stockpile of basic research information faster than it is being added to, particularly since the beginning of World War II. The war had not only greatly stimulated applied research in this country but also dried up most of the basic research in Europe, which had once been the main source for the scientific community. In addition, many of our best university scientists have been attracted away from basic research and teaching by the growing demands of industry and the still more rapid growth of government research during the past eighteen years. This has constituted a double loss, because the men involved were not only those who would other-

* Former Chairman of the Board, Standard Oil Company (Indiana)

203

wise have carried out basic research at the universities, but many of them were also the inspirational teachers who would have attracted and trained the new scientists whom the country needs in increasing numbers. Industry is frequently accused of paying only lip service to the importance of basic research, while following courses of action that make it increasingly difficult for scientists, even in our universities, to concentrate on basic problems as distinct from immediate practical ones.

I need not add my voice to those which have stressed the fundamental importance of better support for basic research, if the country, including its many industries, is to continue to make rapid progress. Such progress is essential for a rising standard of living and the well-being of the whole nation. I believe I can best fulfill my role as a spokesman for industry if I endeavor to discuss what industry has been doing increasingly to support basic research, various methods which have been used to accomplish this result, some of the problems which industry faces in doing more in this area, and some specific suggestions which I hope may prove helpful.

What Industry Is Doing to Support Basic Research

In endeavoring to analyze what industry is doing in this field, we encounter one of the basic difficulties, the lack of reliable quantitative information as to basic research expenditures for industry as a whole. In part this is due to the lack of a clear line of demarcation between basic research and what might be called long-range applied research. I am reluctant to add to the reams which have been written on this subject of definition, but I should like to say that I do not believe that for research to qualify as basic the worker must be entirely disinterested in or oblivious to the possible usefulness of the results of his work. Utter aimlessness should not be considered a particular virtue in this or any other field. Of course, freedom for the scientists to pursue the trail of new scientific knowledge, wherever it leads, and the absence of pressure for early practical results are essential to good basic research. However, I do not believe it should detract from the basic character of a given project if a scientist or an industrial laboratory chooses to work in a field where new fundamental knowledge might prove to have important practical significance. Certainly, if selecting the general field of work because of its possible practical interest bars a given line of research from classification as basic, it would disqualify much of the good basic work that industry is carrying out in its own laboratories.

Two general characteristics of industry research give encouraging testimony to its growing appreciation of the importance of basic research. These are: first, the fact that the longer an industry has been engaged in research, the more it is currently doing in the basic areas; and second, that the older and larger industrial laboratories in the country are, almost without exception, doing a substantially larger proportion of basic research than the many newer laboratories in the same industries. Laboratories such as those of General Electric, American Telephone and Telegraph, and du Pont are but a few of many examples of this trend. This may be due, in part, to the newer laboratories not having yet approached exhaustion of the basic information in their respective fields, but I think the more important factors are that, as a laboratory approaches maturity and acquires a well-rounded staff, the laboratory management appreciates more fully the debt it owes to basic research, and understands that to make really important new advances, basic new knowledge is necessary. Furthermore, the larger and older laboratories are, in general, working closer to the frontiers of their particular fields of science, and that makes the importance of basic research more apparent to them. It is no longer necessary in most companies for the research director to "justify" his basic research program or protect it against encroachment by pressing practical problems. In any case, the two trends I have mentioned are both unmistakable and encouraging.

I trust you will understand if I use research in the petroleum industry to illustrate a number of my points. Not only am I more familiar with that than with any other industry, but it represents a sort of median in the spectrum of industrial research—it was not one of the earliest to embark on a real research program, nor is it one of the "johnny-come-lately's" of which there are so many since World War II. It affords many outstanding examples of what both basic and applied research have meant to the progress of an industry. Its expenditures for all types of research are fairly large—in the neighborhood of $280,000,000 in 1958—but as percentage of the sales dollar (under 1 per cent) they are small compared with those of a number of other large industries. The size of laboratories covers almost the whole range from large to small. The latest figures available show only 2 per cent of the industry's research supported by the federal government.* For all these reasons, I believe it may be considered fairly typical of true industrial research, as distinct from research in industrial laboratories largely supported by the government.

Basic research in our industry really began less than forty years ago, and was, *in part,* from almost the outset, a cooperative effort which other industries might do well to emulate. When the American Petroleum Institute was founded in 1919, there were only thirty or forty chemists or chemical engineers and very few, if any, physicists, doing *any* kind of research in the industry, and most of what they did would today be classed as technical service or quality control. There was practically no

* National Science Foundation, Review of Data #10, May 1958.

basic research—they knew hardly anything about even the chemical composition of the industry's primary raw material.

One of the first acts of the new industry association was to appoint Van H. Manning, former Director of the Bureau of Mines, the A.P.I. Director of Research. With the aid of an advisory committee of educators and industry scientists, of which I had the honor of being the youngest member, a rather ambitious program of research was outlined to be financed cooperatively by the A.P.I. Unfortunately, this program failed to distinguish between basic and applied research, and it was turned down by the Board after a rather prolonged fight in which the majority insisted that research problems should continue to be attacked in the competitive way characteristic of the industry.

Many of the leaders in the industry still felt that the Institute should sponsor and support fundamental research; but the program might never have recovered from this initial setback had not Mr. John D. Rockefeller, in 1925, and the Universal Oil Products Company, shortly thereafter, made their generous offer to donate $50,000 a year apiece for a five-year period to support basic petroleum research if the Institute would furnish the sponsorship and technical guidance. As a result, the first A.P.I. Research Committee of the Board of Directors was set up in January 1926, with a distinguished membership of the industry's leaders under the chairmanship of Walter C. Teagle.

The committee wisely decided at the outset to channel the available funds almost entirely to university and government laboratories. This pattern is still followed. During the initial period, when this program was financed by the two donors, a total of forty-one different fundamental research projects were financed at twenty-five different laboratories, each project being given general guidance by an industry committee of scientists.

207

A crisis arose when these five-year gifts ended at a very unfortunate time—in the depression year of 1931. By this time, however, the value and the propriety of cooperative research on fundamental problems were better appreciated, and the Institute agreed to continue the program on a reduced scale, and to raise funds on a voluntary basis from the industry. For the next five more-or-less depression years the expenditures averaged only about one third of the $100,000-a-year budget of the first five years, and it was deemed necessary to concentrate on a few of the more important projects—selecting the institutions and project directors who had shown particular ability to get results.

Since that time the scope of the work has expanded almost every year until in this fiscal year it includes about thirty projects at an annual cost of $908,000. So far as I can judge, it has the wholehearted support of the entire industry—last year eighty-two companies contributed to its budget.

Of course, the purists might complain that many of these programs, designed to secure fundamental data pertaining to the constituents of petroleum and their reactions, should hardly be classed as true basic research. But when you consider the industry's pitiful lack of information, even as late as 1926, about the origin and composition of its basic raw material, to say nothing about what really takes place in the various processes of refining it, you will realize that it had to start virtually at the beginning. The growing store of information was welcomed and published by the scientific press. Our present program is much more basic, though it is still oriented largely in the direction of learning more about the origin, composition, and fundamental properties of the hydrocarbons and other substances present in the enormously complicated mixture known as petroleum.

This A.P.I. program (all the results of which are published promptly) has yielded to date some 913 scientific and technical papers, 18 books which are standard reference works in thousands of libraries, and 5600 data sheets tabulating the important physical properties of various hydrocarbons and other compounds present in petroleum. Much of these detailed and precise data would never have been obtained by individual companies, and what were obtained would have cost far more, because of duplication of effort. In addition to this, there have been many by-products of this continuing cooperative effort to support basic research. Among them might be cited:

1. There has been stimulation of scientific education by these grants in support of basic research, and it has helped to hold many teachers at universities by giving them modest additions to income or helping to finance needed research apparatus and assistance.

2. Many teachers and graduate students have become better informed about, and interested in, the basic problems of the industry, and much additional research has thereby been stimulated. Many of the graduate students have been attracted into the industry.

3. As the result of the contacts between the university investigators and the industry scientists on the various committees, many of the latter have become more familiar with the methods of basic research, and this has led to more basic research in the industry laboratories. The committee meetings and the hundreds of papers resulting from the work have also proved very stimulating to many, both within and without the industry.

4. Possibly the most important of the indirect results of the program was the impetus it gave to the Petroleum Research Fund, which now finances a somewhat larger amount of even more basic research related to the industry. This fund was established in 1944 by the gift of several large oil companies to

the American Chemical Society of securities which involved practically the whole ownership of Universal Oil Products Company. This company was engaged in developing and licensing refining processes to the oil industry, and the income from this fund gradually increased until in 1958 it contributed approximately $970,000 in over 100 grants for basic research. Early in 1959 the U.O.P. securities were sold to the public and are being replaced by a more diversified list of securities whose total value will be about $70,000,000, which should furnish an annual budget for basic research of about $2,500,000 at the outset. This will probably be a continuing fund. It makes grants mainly to educational institutions on a project basis, and takes precautions to avoid duplication of effort with the A.P.I. fund.

While most of the industry's support of basic research outside its own laboratories is thus channeled through the A.P.I. and the Petroleum Research Fund, on the basis of inquiries from the twelve largest companies in the industry I estimate that in 1958 at least $900,000 additional went directly from the industry to university laboratories for the support of basic research. This does not include the financing of fellowships for graduate students.

The foregoing figures, totaling over $2,800,000 in 1958, are reasonably definite and verifiable as representing our industry's support of basic research *outside* its own laboratories, but the attempt to assemble similar definite figures for the support of basic research *in* those laboratories proved difficult, though I have replies to inquiries from the twelve largest research organizations in the industry. The differences between the figures for basic work reported by the different organizations were almost unbelievable to one who is generally familiar with the caliber of work being carried out by them and the publications resulting therefrom. Also, the figures given me for 1958 by some of the companies were considerably higher than had previously been reported in some private compilations with which I was familiar.

In an effort to determine the reasons for this, I contacted the directors of two of the larger research organizations in the petroleum industry. They attributed the discrepancies largely to the old question of definition. One said that if he classified as basic only research undertaken without any possible practical objective in view, he would have to give a figure only *about one fourth* as great as if he defined it as the search for fundamental knowledge, eventually worthy of publication in scientific journals, and the type of work which would be classed as basic if it were done at a university. A similar view, though with a ratio probably under 2 to 1 instead of 4 to 1, was expressed by the other research director. Since the broader definition fits in better with my own views as expressed near the outset of this paper, I have accepted the figures as reported, though I realize that they are high compared with some earlier compilations. In any case, as expressed in a recent National Science Foundation report, "they represent the summation of judgments of informed reporters at many different vantage points."

With these qualifications, I estimate that the petroleum industry's support of basic research in its own laboratories has increased from $11,100,000 or 7.6 per cent of the $146,000,-000 total in 1953* to about $28,400,000, or 10 per cent of its 1958 estimated research and development expenditures of $280,000,000. To this should be added the $2,800,000 previously mentioned for its financing of basic research outside its own laboratories, which would make a total of about 11 per cent. In the number of scientists engaged in basic research, the comparison would be even more favorable because in general

* National Science Foundation, *Science and Engineering in American Industry*, p. 67.

the cost of applied research and development carries a larger amount of "hardware" than does basic research.

Practically all the research directors contacted agreed that their basic research had been expanding more rapidly than their total research budgets during recent years, in spite of the fact that inflationary factors affect applied research somewhat more than they do basic. Comparing the 1953 with the 1958 figures would indicate that the expenditures for basic research of the larger laboratories in the industry have been increasing at a rate of about 21 per cent per year compared with 14 per cent annual increase for the total cost of all research in the industry. It must again be emphasized that the 1958 figures were obtained from the twelve largest research organizations in the industry, which do about 69 per cent of the country's petroleum refining. These, however, do the great bulk of the *basic* research that is carried out in industry laboratories. Such a rate of increase is quite gratifying, and would seem to indicate that the petroleum industry, at any rate, is making good strides in attaining reasonable balance between basic and applied research.

These figures would at first appear somewhat surprising in view of Dr. Mervin J. Kelly's statement that *total* expenditures for basic research have increased much *less* rapidly over the longer period 1940–1958, possibly by a factor of three, than the total expenditures for research. However, the figures are not necessarily contradictory, because we must realize that the period 1940–1958 was really made up of two periods of widely different character, mainly because of the war.

While accurate figures are not available by years, there is no question but that university research, which comprised well over 50 per cent of basic work, was both curtailed by a shortage of manpower and, to a considerable extent, diverted to defense problems during the war. At the same time, applied research, mainly financed by the government, increased at an unprece-

Under the circumstances, it is quite understandable if the management of such companies feels that it must concentrate for the first ten years or so in catching up with its competitors, becoming thoroughly familiar with the existing literature and technology, and building a capable and well-informed staff to solve the large number of technical problems which any company meets in this fast-moving era. It would find it rather difficult to justify spending any substantial amount of money on basic research during this period. And even if the research director appreciated the desirability of some such program, it takes time to educate a company relatively new to research, and without many technical men in high executive positions. We can hope, however, that such companies would gradually come to recognize both their opportunities and their responsibilities in this field.

Some small laboratories, recognizing both the value of basic research and the difficulty of doing a good job on it in a small laboratory, devote a part of their research budgets to supporting basic work in some university or research institute. This fulfills their obligation to basic research, furnishes ideas and stimulation to their own laboratory, and yet permits the research to be done in an environment more favorable to good basic work. I believe this plan will be increasingly followed. Also, cooperative basic research, like that of the A.P.I., is an excellent way for small companies in various industries to do their part and receive substantial benefit.

Even among the twelve largest laboratories in our industry, I have been surprised to see the great differences in the percentages of their budgets which they report are devoted to basic research in their own laboratories. The percentages range from about 20 down to 2! Part of this difference may be due to the previously mentioned variations in the definition of basic research, and part of it is due to differences in the nature of the operations conducted—more emphasis on petrochemicals and specialty products by some companies versus those who are mainly concerned with production and transportation. Even allowing for those factors, however, there remains a large difference which I think must be attributed to the degree of enlightenment of the management of the various laboratories as to the value, indeed, the necessity, of more basic research in our industry.

I am sure similar differences exist between large laboratories in other industries, and that is one of the reasons for symposiums like this, to make the laggards realize that they are lagging and should do more work in the basic area.

Also, the story of industry's support of basic research would not be complete if we did not recognize the fact that industry and its management have really been *indirectly* responsible for much of the outstanding support given basic research by other organizations. For example, most of the larger foundations, such as Rockefeller, Ford, Sloan, and Carnegie, had their origin in large individual fortunes built up in industry, which were channeled into basic research and other public service by farsighted individuals in corporate management. They were glad to do with their private funds what they had not felt free to do with corporate funds. Also, taxes on industry support much of government research as well, and if corporate taxes were not so high, industry might well support more basic research.

What about the common criticism that industry is too prone to hire away, at fancy salaries, the professors who are so vital to the future of both basic and applied research? Possibly I am not the one to answer that, as I succumbed to one of those offers about 37 years ago. However, the net effect of all this has been to increase greatly the academic salaries of good scientists, which has been beneficial to all. Also, I believe that industry is

better informed as to the hazards of hiring away professors—
one of these hazards is that he may slip out of the laboratory
and end up as Chairman of the Board. I know one company
that is not likely to take that risk again! In any case, the present
trend is toward hiring the professors as consultants, thus gaining the advantage of more contact between basic and applied
research without taking the professor away from his main job.
It is interesting to note in this connection that the pharmaceutical industry recently recommended that the increasing government-financed basic research in that field be channeled into
universities and other nonprofit institutions, rather than into
the industry laboratories.*

When we look at the complete picture, therefore, the
criticism of industry as a whole for failing to give adequate
support to basic research seems less justified than might at first
appear. Certainly, many of our large companies and laboratories are doing all that organizations with the obligation to
make a profit can reasonably justify, and the real task is to
awaken others in industry to a similar appreciation of the facts
of the situation. This is, as I have said, one of the main reasons
for symposiums such as this, and particularly for the wide
dissemination of these papers among those who need them most.

* Official action taken at meeting January 8, 1959, by the Board of
Directors of the Pharmaceutical Manufacturers Association.

Support of
Basic Research
from PRIVATE
PHILANTHROPY

ROBERT S. MORISON
The Rockefeller Foundation

MY TASK is to discuss the role of private philanthropy in the support and encouragement of basic research. One may be allowed to assume that all of us know what basic research is, how to distinguish it from its confusing next-door neighbor, applied research, and how it snobbishly sets itself apart from its so very distant cousins "development" and "technology."

Much less, if anything, has been said so far about private philanthropy, so I propose to give you my own definition. For the purposes of this talk, private philanthropy will mean the giving of money by private individuals to divers good causes out of a love for man. The phrase "money given by individuals" will include money given directly by individuals, or indirectly through foundations, but the major emphasis will be on the latter. Foundations include both the classical sort in which a single person or family dedicates a large personal fortune to the welfare of mankind, and the modern type developed to mobilize a host of widows' mites for the elimination of a single disease. We will not include other sorts of funds to which the term "private" might be applied. For example, support of basic research directly by private industry is not dealt with here since it has been so well discussed by Dr. Fisk, Dr. Wilson, and others.

Philanthropy Defined

The part about a love for man perhaps deserves a word or two of explanation. Philanthropy is frequently equated with charity—the impulse to give something to other people who are worse off than we are. This impulse may arise purely out of pity or it may be complicated by self-interest as when one gives something away to *acquire merit* in the eyes either of one's fellows or of some higher power.

But *love,* on the other hand, may often occur as a transaction between *equals.* When we give a gift to someone we love, we do so partly in the hope of improving something which we feel is already pretty good. A string of pearls to a beautiful girl is in part a tribute to her beauty and in part a way of making her even more beautiful. In the early days of modern science much of the support for basic research stemmed from motives of this sort. When Cosimo II established Galileo as court mathematician and philosopher in Florence, he did so at least in part because he thought Galileo's discoveries and ideas would decorate the court of Florence. Anything which made the court of Florence look good made its reigning duke look even better. But it would be churlish to deny a de Medici the right of acting in response to a more elevated motive. The Renaissance believed, more than we do perhaps, that life could be not only beautiful but magnificent. One reason for loving man was man's magnificent faculty for creating new ways of seeing the world which God has given him. Every man with the power to do so had some sort of an obligation to contribute to the sum total of man's creativeness.

Indeed, it appears that a good part of the early support for basic science was based on this same spontaneous love of creativity for its own sake. Science and art often walked side by side or appeared incorporated in the same person as in the celebrated case of Leonardo da Vinci. The dissecting rooms of the middle Renaissance were as much studio as laboratory. The anatomist in Michelangelo contributed to the realistic power of the bodies which decorate the Sistine Chapel while the artist in Vesalius contrived to make the "Fabric of the Human Body" a delight to the eye as well as a guide to the hand of the skilled surgeon.

The philanthropic spirit which supported such men either by private donation or official appointment was a curious mixture—a love of man combining joy over his creativeness with a very human pride in what he created. Philanthropy as charity is not a marked characteristic of most Renaissance nobles, and the practical application of scientific discoveries was regarded as incidental. For example, one may feel sure that Leonardo would have had no difficulty finding a job even if he had not spent some of his time drawing up plans for fortifications. Galileo was valued as a mathematician and philosopher and only secondarily as an expert on the strength of materials.

Pride is a bad word to us who learned our Christianity from Puritan teachers, and as the most conspicuous consumers in the world, we feel the need of paying La Rochefoucauld's tribute to the virtue of humility. But as Herbert J. Muller—to be described in a group of scientists as "the other Muller"—tells us, one of the uses of the past is to learn from the irony of history. And it is ironical that the million or so Americans who go to Europe each year do so in large part to view the monuments erected to feed the personal pride of the temporal and spiritual leaders of an earlier day. It is difficult to overlook the fact that St. Peter's was constructed largely from profits on the sale of indulgences and Versailles from taxes ground from the poor French peasant. No wonder pride has acquired a bad name, but its long-term results may not be so bad after all. Contrary to Marc Antony's contention, the good that men do sometimes lives after them and the evil, though not perhaps immediately interred with their bones, may be resolved in some less dramatic way. Thus St. Peter's still stands to delight the eye and inspire the spirit long after the sale of indulgences disappeared in the reforms of Luther and John Knox. Versailles has repaid the population of France many times over in tourist gold alone, while the excesses involved in its financing led directly to the establishment of liberté, égalité, and fraternité in one of Europe's first democracies.

Perhaps it would be worth while for us in the twentieth century to recognize that pride does have its good points, that it need not always go before a fall, that it can stimulate us to higher things. We may also take comfort from the fact that drastic changes in our social and economic structure serve to protect society from the worst effects of personal pride and greed.

Individual achievement need no longer rely for its support on money wrung from wretched peasants and sinners. The millions of Americans who voluntarily contributed their dimes to research on polio and heart disease may properly enjoy a quiet pride in having helped fellow Americans to outstanding scientific achievements; and the individual recipients may rest easier in the thought that their support was freely and hopefully given.

It must be confessed that the emphasis given to pride in the foregoing definition of philanthropy is not entirely in accord with traditional practice or indeed with its dictionary meaning. Nevertheless, the original Greek carries no necessary implica-

tion of charity or pity, and it seems at least possible that philanthropists are free to love men in the same way philosophers love
wisdom, or philatelists love stamps, without in some way looking down on them, whatever the dictionary may say.

Philanthropy as a word did not appear in English until
1608, and "philanthropist" not until 1730. By this time men
were becoming aware that relatively few people in society
derived much pleasure or even elementary comfort from life.
The Puritan conscience began to ask itself whether the great
majority of mankind was inevitably predestined to wretched-
ness on this earth. Indeed, the more eccentric began to lay
increasing emphasis on charity as a way of tempering the wind
to the shorn lamb. In England especially, individual gifts and
endowment began to be set up to feed and care for the poor
in various ways. It was this sort of direct service that originally
came to be thought of as philanthropy. The tie-in between
philanthropy and basic research came much later, when it
was found that direct service, provided on the basis of existing
knowledge, would not solve the problem of human misery. The
great philanthropists, the Carnegies, Harknesses, Nuffields,
the Rockefellers, and Tates, were all of them practical men
interested in doing something concrete to help people free
themselves from suffering—hence the great emphasis on health
services in the early days of these endowments.

Utilitarian Aspects of Philanthropy

It is important to remember the utilitarian inheritance of
the private foundations since it still flavors their activities, as
well as those of individual givers and the recently formed
granting agencies of government. It remains difficult to write
an annual report about some new scientific discovery without referring to how it will help to solve some pressing practical
problem. The beauties of phage genetics, for example, must

225

be tied in some way to the cure of cancer or the reduction of the baleful effects of radiation on posterity.

All this is understandable enough in a society which derives its philosophy to such a large extent from the utilitarianism of Jeremy Bentham and our own pragmatist, William James. Carried far enough, however, even this philosophy of practical men can be used to justify the apparently impractical. Basic research is now widely recognized as even more practical than applied, if we only lengthen our time scale a little. Everybody but an occasional Secretary of Defense knows that Faraday's baby grew up into a lusty adult who begat, among other things, the Delco Division of General Motors.

Another thing that has saved the utilitarian background of modern philanthropy from being too harmful is the fact that basic research in the natural sciences had already established a vigorous life of its own long before philanthropy appeared on the scene. We have already alluded to the fact that modern science started hand in hand with the arts as part of the spontaneous desire to glorify man and his works, especially as they were exhibited at the courts and palaces of dukes and cardinals. Long afterwards court physicians and astronomers continued to make basic discoveries purely to amuse themselves and their sovereigns. No one at the time thought that Harvey's description of the circulation had much to do with improving the practice of medicine. Indeed, his practice is said to have suffered seriously after its publication. The Astronomer Royal was supposed to have something to do with setting the clocks of an empire, but in actual fact he devoted much of his time to more basic studies. The first one, James Flamsteed, furnished the "places of the moon" which enabled Newton to lay the foundations of lunar theory.

Private individuals, especially among the landed gentry of England, pursued science out of innate curiosity or in the hope

226

of personal prestige. The founders of the Royal Society were for the most part gentlemen of independent means more interested in the fun of the thing than in practical application or personal profit. Those without private means might find a place in a university or the church, which allowed time for private investigation, but did not require a regular flow of publications as a requisite for promotion. Thus Stephen Hales, the discoverer of the blood pressure, was a Church of England curate, and everybody knows that the founder of genetics was an obscure Austrian monk.

As will be shown later, the great advances of the nineteenth century upon which so much twentieth century application is based came for the most part from university professors. Basic research had in a sense become institutionalized, but the universities of the day still held consciously aloof from the practical everyday world, and their professors were free to follow wherever their fancy led them. The money they needed was not much greater than that provided for teachers in the arts and humanities, and it came in the same way from ancient endowments and block appropriations from government. There appears to have been little tendency to link such support closely to practical applications, and academic freedom to choose individual lines of study was widely respected.

The point in all this is that by the time private philanthropy developed an interest in basic research because of its probable contribution to practical welfare, basic research in the natural sciences was well established as an independent dignified pursuit with its own well-recognized rights and methods. Furthermore, it had built up a large backlog of fundamental knowledge which could be turned almost at once into the practical applications so much sought after by the philanthropists. Large amounts of money could be absorbed by the necessary applied researches with a modest amount left over to

227

help those who kept quietly at work along more traditional lines. As the pressure for quick results began to mount, defenders of older and purer methods emerged to plead the cause of basic research and protect it from semi-annual reports and other pressure. This symposium is perhaps but a particularly explicit and sophisticated battle in the long campaign to maintain the integrity of basic research in the natural sciences.

To summarize: When private philanthropy turned its attention to the natural sciences, it was protected from overindulging its traditional interest in immediate practical objectives by the preexistence of two factors, a substantial amount of accumulated basic knowledge, which could be rather rapidly turned into the machinery of welfare, and a considerable number of basic researchers determined not to be turned away from their first love and more than ready to instruct foundation officers and trustees in the meaning of basic research and academic freedom.

To highlight the importance of the long tradition of impracticality in the natural sciences, we might look for a moment at what happened when philanthropy turned its attention to the social sciences and the allied medical discipline of psychiatry. The practical motivation for entering these fields is clear from the record. For example, a general memorandum dealing with the proposed program of the Laura Spelman Rockefeller Memorial in 1922 included the following paragraphs:

> The need for knowledge of social forces is certainly very great. Not only is it required by social welfare organizations, but by business and industry, and by the agencies of government as well. It is becoming more and more clearly recognized that unless means are found of meeting the complex social problems that are so rapidly developing, our increasing control of physical forces may prove increasingly destructive of human values.
>
> The controlling interest which the Memorial would have in carrying forward such a program would be in no sense an academic

interest in the advancement of social theory and social philosophy; it would be a practical interest in the welfare of individual men, women and children together with a recognition that the knowledge which the social sciences can give is an essential and at the present time inadequately developed means for the achievement of its purposes.

The Rockefeller Foundation embarked on its program in psychiatry with a statement emphasizing the number of hospital beds devoted to mental illness and "the economic, moral, social, and spiritual losses occasioned by the feeble-minded, the delinquents, the criminally insane, the emotionally unstable, the psychopathic personalities. . . ."

All this was true enough but it was perhaps insufficiently noticed that there was not at that time the same backlog of basic research in the social and psychological area that had existed in the natural sciences. A tradition of pure disinterested investigation was also much less clear and well established. It seems particularly difficult for man to study his own behavior without succumbing to the risky temptation to put his partial knowledge to immediate practical use. Thus that great student of human affairs, Niccolò Machiavelli, published his findings not in objective scientific reports but as handbooks for the aid of aspiring princes and courtiers. Nineteenth century economics which got off to a reasonably detached start with Malthus, who was among other things an Anglican curate, soon became involved in practical politics. The next big name is that of Ricardo whose papers on inflation and the Corn Laws led almost immediately to parliamentary discussion and action. Jevons, perhaps the most brilliant of the nineteenth century theoreticians, was equally well known for practical papers on the price of gold and the coal question.

Psychology exhibits a similar tendency to hurry its results into practice as is clearly shown by the ratio of clinical and educational to theoretical or basic psychologists in many of our university departments.

It is of course giving away no secret to say that the last thirty years of foundation support have not brought the same agreed-upon progress in the social as in the natural sciences. Indeed, some observers feel that they detect signs of discouragement on the part of several foundations which formerly conducted broad programs in the behavioral sciences. For example, Bernard Berelson, speaking at the fortieth anniversary of the New School for Social Research, expressed this situation this way:

> The plain fact is that so far as the behavioral sciences are concerned, one foundation after the other has withdrawn from support of the field itself, that is, from basic development of the disciplines in their own terms, and has put what support remains into applications to programmatic concerns of the foundation itself. There has been a constant picture of entry and withdrawal—more so, I think than normal in foundation operations.

Could it be that dissatisfaction with the results is in part due to the error of emphasizing applied at the expense of basic research? Since our interest is in the natural rather than the social sciences, it would be scarcely appropriate to do more than raise the question. Our only excuse for mentioning the subject at all is that the social sciences may serve as the control in testing the hypothesis that foundation support for the natural sciences succeeded, at least in part, because a strong tradition of basic research had already been established long before the foundations entered the field.

Early History of Basic Research

Let us return, then, to a little closer examination of how this tradition became established. Such a historical exercise, brief and superficial though it must be, may give us some clues

230

for deciding how philanthropy might proceed in the future in encouraging the basic research which is so much needed.

One of the first things to be noticed in such a historical review is that basic research really did not require very much money until very recent times. Even today some of the most provocative and general thoughts come from individuals working in restricted space and with relatively simple apparatus. Genetics which started in a monastery garden is even today largely a matter of test tubes, Petri dishes, and conventional microscopes. It is only when we get around to exploring the chemical structure of genes and transforming factors that heavy and expensive equipment becomes essential.

What has always been needed has been curiosity and brains. Conscious philanthropy cannot do much about increasing the supply of curiosity and brains. These are gifts which have to be taken pretty much as they are found. The support of basic research has to focus on providing the opportunity for their use. The support of basic research is in essence then the care and feeding of researchers. How was this done in the past? As far as one can see from a brief and admittedly sketchy survey of the literature the great majority of contributors to basic research fall into the following categories:

1. Pensioners and court appointees
2. Men of independent means
3. Professional people who practiced just enough to supply their physical needs and used their spare time for research
4. University professors

It has not been possible to make any sort of quantitative analysis of the scientific contributions made by these several categories. Perhaps some aspiring Ph.D. student will some day draw an adequate sample and, utilizing the appropriate chi squares and analyses of variance, show us to be completely wrong in our intuitive conclusions. Nevertheless, history reveals that the founders of modern astronomy and physics alone cover all the categories.

Tycho Brahe was born to independent means but also enjoyed a large pension from the king of Denmark. Copernicus was a physician who held a court appointment from his uncle, the Bishop of Ermland. Kepler tried almost every possible means of support; having originally studied for the church, he held a university chair for a short time, married a rich wife, and finally came to be court astrologer to Rudolph the Second in Prague. Indeed, his experience there led him to make an important contribution to our informal investigation into the care and feeding of basic researchers. "Nature," he wrote, "which has conferred upon every animal the means of subsistence, has given astrology as an adjunct and ally to astronomy." Of all these men, Newton probably comes closest to being a good example of the university professor, but as is well known, he spent the later years of his life as Master of the Mint in London.

The fathers of chemistry present an equally varied picture. Sir Robert Boyle, the son of a duke, gives us an outstanding example of the gentleman amateur of private means. Priestley was a clergyman and also received a modest lifelong pension from Lord Shelburne. Lavoisier held a research appointment in the French Academy, but is probably most accurately described as a man of affairs with his experimental farm and his responsibilities for collecting taxes and overseeing the manufacture of gunpowder.

By the nineteenth century, science has become pretty well institutionalized, and the university professor assumes a dominating role in the pursuit of basic science with an occasional Darwin of independent means or an Einstein with his job in the patent office as the exceptions to prove the rule. But it is impressive to note how early in life most of the great ones received what appear to have been secure academic positions. Lacking adequate controls we cannot say whether or not the greatest contributors obtained professorships at ages distinctly lower than the average, but the data do not support the frequently heard remark that Europe traditionally fills her academic chairs with men well past their prime. Nor does the evidence encourage the occasional contention that scientists like prize fighters or ball players do better if they are kept hungry and insecure. Clerk Maxwell was professor at 25; Helmholtz at 28; Faraday, director of the laboratories of the Royal Institution at 34; Rutherford became professor at 27; Bohr at 31; J. J. Thompson was a Fellow of Trinity at 24, and Cavendish professor at 28.

Nor is it only in physics that we find this accent on youth. Schwann, the father of the cell theory, was professor at 28; Pasteur, who developed many of Schwann's observations on spontaneous generation into the foundations of microbiology, was professor at 26; Claude Bernard had to wait to be 42 until he could succeed Magendie as professor of medicine, but had previously been given the newly instituted Chair of Physiology at the Sorbonne. In any case, his career was unusually delayed by his early hope of becoming a playwright. Willard Gibbs, perhaps the only nineteenth century American to achieve equal renown with the Europeans named above, was made professor at 30.

Twentieth Century Basic Research

The progress of science in the twentieth century seems also to be based solidly in institutions. To cite but one index, the overwhelming majority of Nobel prize winners in physics and chemistry were university men. Research institutes contributed a modest share, and more recently industrial laboratories, especially those of the Bell Telephone Company, have entered the list. Amateurs with independent means, private pensioners, or holders of sinecures are entirely absent.

Investigation of the role of private philanthropy in the support of basic research during the modern period must therefore center upon the relations between philanthropy and the university. Furthermore, it will not be a very serious oversimplification if we confine ourselves almost wholly to the United States. Europe has had a long tradition of private giving for public welfare, much of it channeled through religious societies and orders; but the state assumed responsibility both for relief of suffering among the poor and for the conduct of universities much earlier and more extensively than was true in the United States. Private philanthropy abroad thus had less obvious opportunity for action. Differences in tax structure and in more subtle social attitudes combined to keep it from developing the significance it has had in this country.

Contributions to Universities

In the United States, private philanthropy has contributed to basic research in universities in two different ways. The first in time and probably the most important in its results has consisted of direct contributions to general funds. Until relatively recently all our greatest universities were the direct result of private gifts. Many of them indeed bear the names of individuals who started them off with substantial donations. The large foundations organized early in this century tended to make similar unrestricted gifts to universities, especially during the first two decades of their history. Several medical schools were either started or largely reorganized with foundation funds. Even entire universities such as Chicago, Rochester, Duke, Stanford, and Vanderbilt owe their establishment to a combination of large individual donations and foundation funds which allowed them quickly to catch up with institutions founded 200 or 300 years earlier. In line with the "applied" objective which we have found to characterize much private philanthropy in the past, the stated purpose of these early gifts was education rather than research. Nevertheless, the importance of research in connection with higher education was duly recognized and the new institutions provided talented people with secure funds and the freedom to follow their curiosities into the unknown. The essential prerequisites of research were therefore provided in perhaps a sounder way than if the objective had been more explicitly stated and directly sought.

Beginning in the 1920's and extending to the present day, the interest of the private foundations in research became more explicit and direct. The reasons for this change insofar as they can be reconstructed may be outlined more or less as follows.

1. As individuals and especially the larger foundations became more experienced in forwarding the welfare of mankind, they saw more and more clearly the limitations of a policy of direct, immediate, and practical aid to individuals or groups of suffering humanity. It turned out that existing medicines and doctors simply were not up to the job of relieving or preventing most of the troubles from which men suffered. We would have to *know* more before we could *do* more.

2. Coincident with the recognition of the limitations of existing knowledge came a growing awareness of the limitations of foundation funds. The great fortunes of the late nineteenth century had seemed princely in their proportions—which they were—and limitless in their potentialities, which they very distinctly were not. The Carnegie Foundation for the Advancement of Teaching started out with the belief that it could provide suitable pensions for all the college professors in the

235

United States. The Rockefeller Foundation apparently believed that a reasonably successful program for eradicating hookworm in our own southern states could be extended to the borders of the known world. It rapidly became clear, however, that the number of college professors in the United States and the number of hookworms in the world were larger than estimated and that their powers of reproduction were in both cases almost unlimited. Clearly some other power than private charity would have to be called in to meet the quantitative aspects of the problem. It became more and more clearly seen that the role of private philanthropy was that of the pioneer, the explorer, and the designer of pilot projects.

3. Somewhat similarly the task of financing universities and so of providing a secure environment for basic research quickly transcended the resources of private philanthropy.

Under these circumstances it seemed that the foundations could most appropriately select certain individuals whose basic needs were already provided for, and help them to obtain the necessary apparatus and technical help to do a better job. The universities welcomed this new role, even though they regretted the passing of the large gifts for endowment, at least in part because it relieved them of the difficulty of drawing invidious distinctions within their own faculties. Furthermore, it was recognized that universities, like other institutions, are more or less set in a traditional mold and find it difficult to readjust budgets and personnel to meet the needs of new and rapidly expanding fields of study. The absence of long-term commitment to individuals or to classical disciplines makes the foundations far quicker on their feet. For example, as the interests of a new generation of biologists shifted away from morphology and taxonomy to the biophysical world of the large molecule, the foundations could help provide the increasingly expensive instrumentation without disturbing the peace of the natural history museum. Left to their own devices the universities could not have responded nearly so quickly or extensively to the needs of these newer basic researches. In most cases the universities welcomed such outside help and, after a preliminary transition period financed with risk capital from the foundations, they gratefully shouldered more and more of the load themselves. It is worth while remembering, however, that outside help is not always welcomed by university administrators. There have been times when professors and presidents have been enticed into following the enthusiasm of some foundation officer into areas which turned out less productive than had been hoped or more expensive than had been estimated. Discomfort and even pain have sometimes been felt on both sides when the day came for the foundation to withdraw its support and the university found itself unable or unwilling to carry on as expected.

On the whole, however, the grant-in-aid programs for the promotion of newly developing areas of basic research were well received and constituted the typical activity of private foundations from about 1925 right down to the present day. After World War II it was these programs which presumably formed the templates upon which the postwar programs of the government granting agencies were fashioned.

The private foundations also set a pattern for an even more direct attack on the care and feeding of research workers. The grant-in-aid programs, helpful though they no doubt have been for outstanding people already well established in research posts, did not necessarily ensure a sufficient supply of basic investigators. The fellowship programs for postdoctoral candidates were designed to preserve for research outstanding individuals who might otherwise be drawn into other pursuits at a critical point in their careers. As we have seen above, the outstanding investigators of the nineteenth century typically achieved professorial status before they were thirty. By the twentieth century the average age for obtaining a permanent appointment seems to have risen by five or even ten years. It is difficult to say whether this change is due to a failure to provide enough professorial posts, to an increasing reluctance to take risks on the part of academic institutions, or to the increasing complexity of science which demands a longer period of maturation before a man can be qualified to hold a senior post. Whatever the reason, it was at any rate clear by about 1920 that something would have to be done to provide support for those who wished further research experience after obtaining their doctorates. The first large-scale effort designed to meet this critical need was the fellowship program instituted by the National Research Council shortly after World War I. This program, portions of which are still in existence, has been supported almost entirely by private funds and has by general agreement been outstandingly successful.

For a time after the war the conventional one- or two-year fellowships provided by the NRC were supplemented by an additional program of more advanced fellowships of longer duration for men entering a career of academic medicine—the Welch fellows. A little later the John and Mary Markle Foundation embarked on its currently distinguished program of support for men in the middle passage between doctorate and professorial chair.

Again, as was the case with the grant-in-aid programs of the classical foundations, their fellowship programs have served as a stimulus and model to the newly formed private foundations and government granting agencies.

The vast expansion of fellowship funds and special grants made possible by these newer sources of research funds have done much to increase the flow of qualified people into research both basic and applied. In many research groups the number of people provided for by outside funds of this sort far exceeds the number of regular institutional appointments. This situation has of recent years begun to raise questions in the minds of academic administrators and others responsible for the progress of science. The temporary nature of most of their support is a constant source of anxiety not only to the people so supported but also to the professors and deans who share the responsibility for their appointments but lack control over the necessary funds.

In pointing this out we are not merely asking for sympathy for those burdened by personal or administrative uncertainties. It seems more than likely that such uncertainties interfere seriously with the progress of basic research. Young men are constantly put under pressure to select sure fire problems, the solution of which can easily be foreseen and published. Almost by definition such problems are less basic than the vaguer more puzzling questions which take unhurried time and reflection merely to ask. The urge to publish almost anything that can be called new, whether or not it is significant, has further baleful effects. It overstuffs our journals, overloads the stacks of our libraries, and gags those who still try to swallow the ever increasing flow of what is so politely referred to as literature. The high ratio of temporary junior workers to established senior investigators puts serious administrative and teaching burdens on the latter. It thus develops that many of our best and most original minds become preoccupied with the business aspects of science at the very moment when in happier times they became free to give the bulk of their energy to unfettered research.

Fortunately, the situation is increasingly being recognized and steps are being taken to change matters. Grants are being given for longer periods of time and with fewer strings attached. Fellowship appointments are being lengthened, and quite recently three of the leading categorical foundations have come up with a new invention to assure "support throughout their productive lives to outstanding scientists of proved capacity and brilliance." Sometimes referred to as career investigatorships, these positions are essentially research professorships guaranteed "without limit of time" by the foundation. The commitment is directly to the individual, but the arrangements are usually carefully worked out with the institution in which the individual is working, and the latter undertakes to provide laboratory space and certain other amenities. Although such schemes can be criticized for diffusing a responsibility which should rest fully in the university, they have many merits. At the very least they restore to a few professors "the time and freedom to develop potentially fruitful ideas, [and] to follow new leads as they emerge." Supported as they are by organizations which command wide support from the public, they serve to draw public attention to what after all is the *sine qua non* of basic research—men with the capacity and opportunity to do it. It would obviously be unfortunate if the day should come when a substantial proportion of the senior men in our universities owed their primary loyalty to some extraneous body. Before that day comes we may be allowed to hope that the autonomy of our universities may be restored through an increase of unearmarked funds. Meanwhile the career investigatorships may help tide basic research over some rough spots and call attention to the need for university professors who are professors and not some new kind of dean.

Government and Private Philanthropy

We now may pause to notice that private philanthropic support for basic research has come full circle. It began in the United States 300 years ago with the efforts of wealthy private individuals who set up and fostered our great private universities. During the first 200 years the research output was small indeed, but at least the environment was there and when

America became of age intellectually after the Civil War, basic research began in earnest. In our own century, private philanthropy began to organize itself first in the form of foundations established by a single person or family. The last two decades have seen the growth of organized funds whose roots penetrate almost every household and schoolroom in the country. The individual or family foundations at first tended to carry on the earlier tradition of contributing to the general funds of universities, but later turned more and more to the selection of individuals and projects for special attention. This focusing or concentration of financial aid on problems of topical interest came to be even more emphasized by the categorical funds. Finally, we are beginning to see that we cannot indefinitely depend on the tree of knowledge to produce the apples which keep the doctor away unless we do something about the health of the tree itself. It seems particularly significant that the categorical funds with their announced interest in the application of knowledge to specified diseases should have preceded their older brothers in recognizing the need to do something about the indirect costs of research and finally in restoring the opportunity for free-wheeling scholarship to the university professor.

The growth of organizations like the National Fund for Medical Education and the recent move on the part of the United Funds to devote a certain percentage of their collections to the general support of medical schools through the National Fund should also be noted. Such moves encourage the hope that private philanthropy in the broadest sense is disposed to return a larger measure of responsibility for the progress of science to the men in our universities who are actually carrying the burden in the heat of the day.

It remains only to make what guesses we can about the role of the private philanthropist in the future. Like everything else these days, private philanthropy is living in a rapidly changing world. Federal support for scientific research in colleges and universities was approximately $15,000,000 in 1940, and in 1958 was something like $440,000,000. The answer to what proportion of this is basic research depends on whom you ask. C. V. Kidd has recently noted that research workers themselves estimate the amount of basic research at a figure approximately double the one provided by the government agencies which supply the funds. Perhaps we may content ourselves with the general statement that the amount of money available for the support of basic research is large. Many experienced people will tell you that no first-class investigators, and very few competent ones, need suffer for lack of research funds if they have the foresight and are willing to take the trouble to ask for them on time. Doubtless, too much of this money is still doled out in packages with labels which are too explicit and for times which are too short to allow adequate flexibility and planning. But measures have been taken to correct these difficulties. Procedures now under study in Washington make it likely that a satisfactorily large proportion of funds will be distributed for long periods of time and with few restrictive strings attached.

The time is very nearly here when private philanthropy will no longer be distinguished from public support by the greater flexibility and duration of its grants. What then? The categorical funds like the Heart Association and the Cancer Society, as we have seen, have pretty clearly drawn missions and have shown an admirable capacity to adapt their policies to rapidly shifting situations. The money put at their command by a generous public is respectably large in relation to their restricted missions. For the foreseeable future there seems little danger that they will find themselves elbowed into an insignificant corner by the increasing growth of government funds.

The situation of the classical private foundations is somewhat different. The major ones are not restricted to any special subject or field and the proportion of their annual incomes available for basic research is relatively small when measured against other sums spent for the same purposes.

Two recent reports on the state of research give attention to the future role of private foundations and specifically deplore the "hesitancy of private foundations to maintain the level of their contributions to scientific research in academic and other non-profit institutions." Both of them go on to suggest special sorts of activities which may be most appropriate for private foundations. For example, the report of the President's Science Advisory Committee points to "a vital and unique role . . . in supporting imaginative and audacious research that industry or government may not always support."

Similar statements implying unusual insight and/or courage to private foundations are frequently made and they are of course not particularly difficult for foundation officers and trustees to accept. But are they really true?

Underlying such statements is the tacit assumption that the most imaginative research is in some sense frightening and upsetting. Many bona fide examples of the frightening nature of new ideas can be cited from the history of science. The founders of the heliocentric theory certainly ran into trouble on these grounds; the shy and retiring Darwin needed a Huxley to run interference against the massed Wilberforces of his day. Semmelweis was driven mad by the conservative opposition of his superiors in Vienna. But it is difficult to find similar examples in the recent history of the natural sciences. Einstein was made Ausserordentlich professor within four years of his first paper on the special theory of relativity. The destroyers of parity received Nobel prizes almost immediately after letting their results become known. The general public reads calmly of experiments which overthrow the doctrine of the individuality of the gene. In a word we have become used to the tentative nature of natural science and are inclined to expect that today's truth will soon become tomorrow's special case. The real difficulty confronting foundation officers and others responsible for the selection of imaginative research is of a different sort. Sometimes, but actually not nearly so frequently as is often supposed, imaginative people are odd characters who make trouble for their superiors. In occasional instances their anxiety to make a real leap into the future causes them to overlook certain traditional niceties in experimental method in a way which gives their work an initially uncertain and inelegant character. By the usual criteria the work simply doesn't look very good. Maybe the worker has an additional tendency to overlook evidence already in the literature which tends to throw doubt on the big new idea. Indeed, the most original and inventive person I happen to know has told me that he never tells his friends about a new idea until he has worked on it for some time. If he did, he feels sure that they would think up any number of perfectly valid reasons for believing it to be no good.

It is situations such as this that give foundation officers and other research underwriters their gray hairs. Boldness is indeed needed to pick out and support the new idea brought in by the relatively untried investigator. But where does boldness end and recklessness begin? After all, the boards and staffs of foundations hold their funds as a public trust and by temperament are far too conscientious to gamble continuously. Actually it is not immediately obvious why the private foundations should be any bolder than the government agencies in dealing with the possibly highly original project which does not meet the usual methodological criteria. Indeed the case can be made that the government agencies are frequently in a better position to take risks. In some fields these agencies now have so much money that they are almost forced to gamble with some of it.

But let us return to the first type of boldness, the courage to back people with ideas which are upsetting or frightening to the general public or some vested interest. Although the opportunities for exercising such courage are now rare in natural science, there are still plenty of them in the social sciences. And the situation is certainly made no easier by the fact that most projects dealing with the behavior of man require the second kind of boldness too. For it is undeniable that many original investigations in this area do not meet all the methodological criteria one can think up. Freud pretty much dreamed up his own method and no one even today is quite sure of its validity; Kinsey, who at least confined himself much more completely to the scientifically respectable act of counting events in a presumably real world, was vulnerable in his sampling procedures and very likely overrated the validity of his interviewing methods; the behaviorist Watson obviously underrated the importance of genetic factors. And so it goes, until those who for one reason or another have hoped to do something to better our knowledge of our own behavior wonder whether we are forever doomed to finding that the important investigations are unsound and the sound ones unimportant.

Here at least is a real opportunity for boldness. For some time to come government will have special difficulties in sponsoring research which is likely to challenge long cherished beliefs about the ordering of behavior. Private philanthropy should in theory at least be able to find the courage to defend the right to ask questions and to stick by the questioners while they flounder around hunting for the appropriate techniques. In order to do this properly, the foundations and indeed many of the researchers themselves should be encouraged to put their interest in practical application away on a high shelf. In a word, research in the social sciences should become basic research.

At the risk of breaking one of the real rules of the game one might even go so far as to suggest that the foundations develop the boldness to interfere ever so slightly with the work of their own grantees. One thinks here of the possibility of encouraging investigators to relinquish their urge to stress practical applications and to avoid unnecessarily melodramatic methods of procedure.

It need not be regarded as a shocking interference with academic freedom to suggest that a pure scientist has no real obligation to publish his findings on the frequency of sodomy in every magazine in the country, or that there may be satisfactory ways of studying decision making in small groups short of inserting microphones in jury rooms.

Support of Undergraduate Colleges

Finally are there other vital roles for the private foundations in an affluent society? The President's Advisory Committee mentions provision for fellowships and more permanent positions in new specialties and interdisciplinary areas and the maintenance and establishment of first-rate graduate schools. Both of these are traditional activities which have been discussed above.

In a special paragraph the report points to the importance of undergraduate colleges. On the whole it would appear that foundations and indeed most sources of support except for handfuls of loyal alumni have not given sufficient attention to these institutions. Many of them, as clearly shown in the well-known study by Knapp and Greenbaum have turned a wholly disproportionate number of their graduates toward productive work in the sciences. It seems most unlikely that they can continue this record unless they can provide the sort of research facilities which attract the most stimulating teachers. Several other important considerations that argue for the active encouragement of research in our liberal arts colleges should not be overlooked. It seems quite probable, for example, that there still exists a certain number of excellent scientists who for one reason or another feel ill at ease as members of large research teams and who will do their best work in a calmer, more reflective atmosphere. Furthermore, an important fraction of our future business leaders and men of affairs receive their preparation for life in liberal arts colleges. Even though they take only the required minimum of science courses, it is important that they have an opportunity to see real live scientists at work and to recognize them as reasonably normal members of any community. Increasingly, people in all walks of life have to take personal and public decisions which involve science in one way or another, and it seems more than merely worthwhile to provide them with early opportunities for seeing what science is all about. Finally the presence of working scientists in the smaller towns in which many of our liberal arts colleges are situated should have a salutary effect on the surrounding community. Through Rotary Club talks and occasional articles in the local press, they could provide a personal touch which would help the average citizen to view science as organized common sense and not some sort of magic carried on in palaces and castles in certain capital cities.

Another important area (one not mentioned by the committee) in which private foundations have some important advantages and opportunities is the forwarding of basic research on an international or worldwide basis. The need for developing basic research as a background for technical advance in many underdeveloped areas of the world is so obvious as to need no special analysis here. Governments and private agencies are already embarked on programs designed to this end.

In many areas of the world aid from foreign governments is looked upon with some suspicion. Private agencies are, however, welcomed and incidentally provide object lessons of the importance of private initiative to societies which lack such tradition. The recognized disinterestedness of private philanthropy may be especially useful in the organization of international research projects requiring cooperation of investigators in different areas. Such programs are still rather rare but there are tempting possibilities for developing productive work on malnutrition, the incidence of atherosclerosis, and the control of epidemics on an international basis.

With all these possibilities before it, private philanthropy need not worry about being overshadowed by the growth of tax-supported aid to basic research. Indeed it might rather welcome being relieved of some of its more conventional assignments. Freed in this way it might even try to recapture some of the elan, the pride, the joy in supporting creativeness which characterized the Renaissance patrons of science mentioned at the beginning of this paper.

THE SUPPORT OF BASIC RESEARCH

Summary of the Symposium

DAEL WOLFLE
*American Association for
the Advancement of Science*

INDUSTRY and government have learned that research is one of modern man's most powerful tools—a tool that creates new products, new weapons, new cures for disease, new services, new demands, and new wealth. The return on the research dollar is so great that industry and government are increasing, year after year, the amount invested in research and development. The total has now reached an annual rate of $10 billion and will surely increase in the years ahead.

Industry and government have also learned—but with less assurance and universality—that it is prudent to invest some of their research dollars in studies that are not aimed directly at the solution of immediate practical problems, but that are

249

intended to strengthen and broaden the fundamental scientific foundation from which practical applications grow.

As money and emphasis on research and development have increased, one consequence is that research has taken on some of the aspects of big business. These aspects are tending to overwhelm the scientific curiosity that is fundamental to the whole development of research. Of the $10 billion a year, too small a percentage, less than a tenth, goes for basic research.

Increased support for research and development has frequently clouded the distinctions between basic and applied research, and between these two activities and the engineering developments that grow from them. In the process of rapid expansion of industrial and military technology, the critical importance of gaining fundamental new knowledge from research has tended to be obscured by the urgent competition of pressures for the maintenance of national security and the promotion of industrial growth, personal health, and national welfare. It is therefore not surprising that there is confusion over the differences between basic and applied research and uncertainty about the special role and special problems of basic research as a means of gaining fundamental new knowledge.

The purpose of the Symposium on Basic Research was to let the nation know of the special needs of basic research and its relationship to our future national strength and to recommend methods by which the nation might make more effective use of its potential resources for basic research.

The Importance of New Knowledge

J. Robert Oppenheimer, the first speaker, gave a double justification of the search for fundamental new knowledge: "New knowledge is useful" and "the getting of it is ennobling." There is so much evidence of the usefulness—often the quite unexpected and unpredictable usefulness—of new and fundamental knowledge that Crawford Greenewalt and other speakers concluded that basic research findings almost always turn out to be useful. Oppenheimer himself found two exceptions: "I should think that as of today, Einstein's general theory of relativity has had few, if any, practical consequences . . . . Again, as far as I know, the analytical theory of numbers, as such, has led to no practical consequences." The speakers agreed, however, that "one must think hard and long to find examples like this." And even these may eventually turn out to have practical consequences.

Several of the industrial participants went beyond the general social usefulness of new knowledge and the basic research that produces it, to point out that industry profits directly from participation in basic research. James Fisk urged industry to engage in basic research in order better to be able to understand basic findings wherever made and to appraise them in terms of their usefulness to industry. William Baker developed the points that a knowledge of fundamental scientific theory is necessary to guide practical research, and that such knowledge extends the range of understanding and usefulness of research findings, whether those findings are initially classed as basic or applied. The same principles apply to government laboratories.

This, then, is one of the reasons for emphasizing basic research: it brings understanding, and understanding is useful. In fact, it has often been said that basic research is the most practical kind of research. In the words of President Eisenhower, "achievements in basic research, adding as they do to man's fundamental understanding, have a quality of universality that goes beyond any limited or local application [and] eventually . . . benefit all mankind." If the nation and the scientific community are not now devoting as much of their resources to basic research as they might, the most severely practical considerations dictate a shift of emphasis and support to more basic research.

But practical considerations are not the only justification for basic research or for providing adequate support for those who wish to explore the boundaries of nature. Perhaps the most distinctively human characteristic of man is that he asks questions about the past and the future, the very small and the very large, the nature of life, and the reasons for his existence and for the events and objects of which he is a witness. Each using his own special vocabulary, the poet and artist, the religious leader, the philosopher, and the scientist all ask essentially these same questions. Because of their special interests or special knowledge, these men ask more penetrating questions than most men, and often reach more illuminating answers. But all men ask such questions, even though fumblingly and uncertainly, and all are therefore helped by the special skill of scholar, poet, artist, and theologian. Such men are leaders of the intellectual, esthetic, and spiritual realms, the realms in which man is most distinctively human.

It is in this sense that the getting of new knowledge is ennobling. Because it is, the quest deserves the best and most imaginative effort of scholars—and deserves the adequate and appropriate support of society.

The support of society is given to individual scientists. But in the ultimate sense, the support is not for scientists as individuals but rather for society as a whole. The usefulness of science is to society rather than to the individual scientist, and the ennobling quality of the search for new knowledge contributes to the whole of society. In asking that his work be adequately supported, the research scholar is asking for opportunity to be of greater service to society.

Which of these reasons, the usefulness of basic research or

its ennobling quality, is the more important? The two are incommensurable, and there can be no answer. The research scholar deeply engrossed in a problem may be carried forward by the sheer intellectual excitement of probing nature's secrets. Other persons may take most satisfaction in the practical result. Neither is wrong. Both reasons are good.

Basic and Applied Research

If words could talk, *research* would surely complain of being overworked. The word is used to describe the scholarly activities of a Nobel laureate and to give prestige to such immediately useful records as counting the customers of a chain store. It may in one sentence be used to describe the search for the laws of nature and in another the search for facts to support a conclusion already reached.

Even if the misuses are left out of consideration, a wide range of activities can properly be described as research. Within this wide range, various adjectives are used to describe special types of research. *Basic* research and *applied* research are the most familiar, but there are others, such as practical research, developmental research, programmatic research, or materials research. All these terms are useful, but none has sharp boundaries, and one cannot be cleanly separated from another. From watching a scientist at work, it would frequently be quite impossible to decide which adjective most accurately described his research.

Yet there are real differences between types of research. A scientist sometimes explicitly seeks information that will help to solve a practical problem. He wants to cure a disease, to develop a drought-resistant plant, to design a nose cone that will not burn up on reentering the atmosphere, to build an atomic power plant. The motivation to contribute to a specific practical need may be so strong that the scientist willingly disregards

253

otherwise interesting scientific leads. Under certain industrial or military circumstances, the researcher is under some degree of compulsion to stick closely to an assigned problem. These examples illustrate applied research; the methods and knowledge of science are in these cases being applied to solve practical problems. Yet it must be remembered that not infrequently certain pieces of fundamental knowledge needed for the solution of a practical problem may be totally lacking and must be acquired before further progress on the practical problem can be achieved; thus what is commonly called applied research often involves some component of basic research.

Sometimes all the scientist seeks is understanding. What he learns may well turn out to be useful. If it is, usually he is pleased, but usefulness is not his goal. His goal is to learn more about the nature of things. He seeks to extend man's knowledge. He is engaged in basic research.

The purpose of all scholarly activity, including research, is to develop the structure of knowledge. To this end, both applied and basic research contribute. Moreover, there is constant interaction and reciprocal fertilization between the two. Basic research provides a firm foundation for practical applications, and applied research may lead to beautiful basic science. The practical problems of aviation necessitated studies that have greatly extended man's fundamental knowledge of fluid mechanics. When Pasteur was asked to try to save the silkworm industry of France—surely a practical problem—he used a basic research approach that yielded information of fundamental importance to biology and medicine. The productivity of an earlier American scientist was attributed by one reviewer to "the combination of an enviable analytic power with sturdy practical experience." Of science in the large it is also true that the interplay of the analytic power of basic research and the sturdy practical experience of applied work lends strength to both.

One of these is not a higher, or a better, kind of research than the other, but there is some separation of responsibility for the two. In the main, universities and some of the private research institutions concentrate on basic research, while industrial and government laboratories emphasize applied research. There is overlap, however, and although the generalization is reasonable and useful, there is no sharp cleavage between institutions that engage in basic research and those that engage in applied research.

There are also differences between the two research areas in their support and popular appeal. The amount of money spent on applied research and development is ten or twenty times as great as the amount spent to broaden and deepen knowledge of the workings of nature. In part, this difference results from the inherently greater costs of much applied work, and in part from a greater popular interest in applied research. It is easier to understand, and therefore easier to support, an effort to improve the preparation of polio vaccine or to extend the range of a radar network than it is to understand the biochemistry of heredity or the fall of parity.

There are no sharp divisions between basic and applied research, yet even imperfect distinctions and definitions are useful. A considerable number of symposium participants struggled with the problem of defining basic research.

Problems of Definition

The difficulty in agreeing on definitions results from the fact that basic and applied research inevitably overlap each other, not only in one dimension, but in several. Thus, suggested criteria of differentiation always get confused. The motivation of the scientist is one such criterion. When research is intended to add to fundamental scientific knowledge, it is called basic research. When it is intended to solve a practical problem, it is called applied research. But the results must also be considered. Some research turns out to be of far-ranging importance, and is therefore called fundamental or basic. Other research discovers something of practical usefulness, and is called applied. These labels may be used regardless of the scientist's purpose or motivation. A commercial chemist may seek means of improving the drying qualities of a paint, and in the course of his work discover something fundamental about molecular layers. Was he engaged in basic or applied research?

Another criterion sometimes used is the freedom of the investigator to follow his own ideas and the leads that turn up in the course of his work. If he is completely free in this respect, his work is sometimes called basic research. But the man who seeks a solution to a practical problem, for example a problem in medicine, may have equal freedom to follow his own ideas and research leads.

Sometimes the quality of the work gets involved in the distinction. If the results are broadly important, they are likely to be called fundamental or basic. (If the results are trivial, the work is not called applied, but neither is it likely to be called basic.) This usage further complicates the problem of distinguishing between basic and applied research.

Despite these difficulties, it is often desirable for statistical and accounting purposes to distinguish basic from applied research. In explaining the importance of basic research to boards of directors, to members of Congress, or to the public, it is obviously necessary to have some common understanding of what is being talked about. The definition of the National Science Foundation uses the scientist's motivation as the criterion: "Basic research is that type of research which is directed toward increase of knowledge in science. It is research where the primary aim of the investigator is a fuller knowledge or understanding of the subject under study, rather than a practical application thereof." Another definition, discussed in some detail by the participants, also used the scientist's motivation as its criterion: "Basic research is the never-ending search for better understanding of man himself and of the total world, animate and inanimate, in which he lives. The drive which stimulates basic research is man's insatiable curiosity concerning the unknown, and the intellectual and aesthetic satisfaction that comes from understanding."

Another proposed definition included both motivation and results: "The 'basic' classification is adopted where it is thought that the *immediate* purpose or result is to contribute to the sum of scientific knowledge, whereas the 'applied' classification is adopted where it is thought that the *immediate* purpose or result is to forward some contemplated line of action."

None of these and no other proposed definition survived the criticism of the symposium participants. Yet inability to agree on a precise definition does not interfere with communication. For it is only at the boundaries that there is confusion; except at the boundary between basic and applied research it is generally quite clear which of the two is meant.

There were two opposed reactions to the whole attempt at definition. One group thought the effort to agree upon a precise definition would be very difficult but thoroughly worth while. The other group thought the effort not worth while. The latter point of view prevailed.

One participant proposed a clarifying geographical analogy. Everyone knows in a general way the location of the Midwest and the Far West, but no one can locate an exact dividing line between these regions. A biologist offered another analogy. It is usually easy to tell the difference between a plant and an

257

animal, but a few marine animals "look" like plants, and among the simple one-celled organisms there are some that puzzle the biologists, for the usual distinctions break down.

So it is with research. Exact boundaries defy definition, but for practical purposes the difference between basic and applied research is real and useful.

What Arrangements Will Best Support Basic Research?

Granting that new knowledge leads to practically useful inventions, and that the search for new knowledge is one of man's highest and most distinctively human pursuits, how can the search for new knowledge best be fostered? There is no single way, no single golden path to research success. There are many ways to strengthen and support basic research, for basic research is a varied activity, carried out under varied conditions. The answers given by symposium participants fall naturally into three groups.

First, the *general intellectual environment* in which a scholar works clearly forms one of the conditions that determines whether or not his work will find the intellectual response and financial support necessary for growth and maturity.

Second, the *educational environment* is important, particularly in the long-range view. Research is a continuing, cumulative venture, with one man building upon another's work, and one generation correcting, refining, and extending the work of the previous generation. The quality of the next generation of research scholars is dependent upon the quality of the educational system in which they are now being trained.

Third, the immediate *research environment*—the conditions under which a scientist works and the extent to which he is allowed to choose the problems he will investigate, enabled to communicate with other scientists, assisted by the special devices, technical specialists, and scientists from other fields that his particular work requires—all of these and similar administrative, financial, organizational, and cultural variables help to determine both the amount and the quality of basic research.

These three parts of the answer to the question *What arrangements will best support basic research?* are the subject of the remainder of this summary.

The Intellectual Environment

When the authors of *The Pursuit of Excellence,* the Rockefeller Brothers Fund report on American education, looked back over the span of history, they reached the provocative generalization that a society gets the kind of excellence it understands and appreciates. The raw, rebellious, revolutionary American Colonies produced great and enduring political theory and political institutions, but not the great art being produced in Europe of the same period.

The quantity and quality of research depend upon the total social and intellectual life of the nation. As a consequence of general agreement on this relationship, much of the discussion was centered on the problem of achieving broader general appreciation of scholarship, and broader understanding of the importance of the total search for new knowledge. Speaker after speaker emphasized the importance of developing the right climate for research, and speaker after speaker asserted that in the effort to develop this climate science does not stand alone. Science is part of scholarship, of intellectual effort, and the climate conducive to basic research is the climate conducive to scholarship generally. At one point, the chairman interrupted the discussion with the summarizing statement that "The subject we are dealing with goes beyond any of the sciences. The subject we are dealing with is scholarship." President Eisenhower, in his dinner address, reminded the participants that the

259

health of science depends upon the health of the nation's total intellectual and educational effort.

In the insistent repetition of this theme, the participants were not merely making polite bows in the direction of the humanities and arts, but were expressing a profound conviction that both the narrower viewpoint of science and the broader viewpoint of man's total intellectual, cultural, and spiritual life make it essential that the nation appreciate and cultivate intellectual and educational excellence, broadly, at all levels, and in all fields. This conclusion was given added emphasis a few days later in the White House statement on education in America, as it had been the central theme of the Rockefeller report, *The Pursuit of Excellence,* a year earlier.

It is not easy to change the climate of opinion, but some steps can be taken. Part of the symposium discussion was aimed directly at scientists. Several speakers pointed out that the scientist himself is partly to blame for the fact that the general public does not understand and appreciate basic science. The research scientist too frequently avoids, rather than seeks, opportunities to explain science. If he does try to explain, he is ever likely to talk of end products and applications, for these, he knows, will be understood. It is, one of the speakers contended, the responsibility of the scientist to do all he can to impart to others the processes, the wonder, and the beauty, as well as the facts and uses, of science.

It is difficult to explain what is going on in the forefront of science to one who does not have the vocabulary, who does not understand the techniques or theory, and to whom the questions being explored seem remote from everyday reality. It is difficult, but it is easier in some fields than in others. In fields of science which have not yet ranged as far from common experience as have nuclear physics and cosmology, the research worker usually has less difficulty in explaining not only the facts and uses but also the wonder, the beauty, and the processes of science. The symposium said to all scientists, *"Get busy on this task."*

Industry has a special opportunity to help to change the climate of opinion. For industry has high prestige in a heavily industrialized society. Consequently the statements that industrial leaders make about science, the support they give to basic research, the form in which industrial grants to universities are made, and the way in which they are announced are all important in creating the climate of popular opinion.

The climate of opinion could also be influenced by the more balanced use of money. Newspaper headlines and budget statements have emphasized again and again the billions of dollars being spent on science. But there are not billions spent on basic science; the amount is only a small fraction of the total—ten, or six, or perhaps as little as four per cent, depending upon how one defines basic research. In public press and in official statements, the lumping together of science and technology, of basic and applied research, confuses the public, and conceals both the differences between basic and applied research and the relative support going to each.

The role of the university in research has been affected by this imbalance. Through financial necessity and as a result of governmental and industrial pressure, they have been forced into increased engagement in applied research. This change in university research activity has probably contributed to the general confusion between basic and applied research.

A better balance between basic and applied work and a better balance between science and other fields of scholarship would help to alter the climate of opinion. One participant, in a particularly vigorous statement, proclaimed that "We ought to encourage the old tradition of the university scholar biting the hand that feeds him and telling society, 'We do not think

261

that you properly understand your own needs. We do not think that the continued support of science alone is going to give you what you want and what you ought to have.'"

Money is needed for scientific research, and under current procedures scientists frequently have to devote a good deal of time to the task of getting adequate support. But the vehement statement just quoted and a good many other like-minded statements clearly said to government, to industry, and to other sources of support, *"In the interests of science, and in the interests of society, don't concentrate your financial support exclusively on science. Concentrate on intellectual quality and on helping universities to become broadly excellent."*

Higher Education—The Long-Range Problem

"Basic researchers will either come out of higher education or they are not going to exist. They do not come out of attics." In these words a college president reminded his symposium colleagues that although it is of the utmost importance to consider the conditions that will best foster basic research now, it is of at least equal importance to consider the source and quality of the nation's future research scientists.

It has often been observed that the best teacher is one who is also a student. The scholar who is exploring the unknown is adding to his and to the world's store of knowledge. His zeal for scholarship enlivens his teaching and inspires his students. It is good for teachers to be researchers. But researchers must also be teachers if they are to be followed by another generation of good researchers.

At the graduate level, interplay between teaching and research is the normal custom. The graduate faculty typically consists of scholars who are actively engaged in both teaching and research. Even the research professor who holds no formal classes teaches his graduate students and junior colleagues. The students profit and so do the teachers; many a research idea was born in the lively discussion of teacher and student.

Liberal Arts Colleges

In the liberal arts college, however, the situation is sometimes sadly different. The special problems of the liberal arts colleges was the subject of Laurence Gould's paper. The evidence he presented of the extent to which some liberal arts colleges fail to provide time and recognition for research on the part of their faculty members gave serious warning for the future.

Education is downgraded if the teachers are not able to engage in sufficient research to keep themselves intellectually alive and up to date. A liberal arts college frequently cannot, and normally should not, aspire to become a graduate university, and its research activities must be on a different scale from those of the large universities. Yet if lack of time, lack of money, and lack of facilities are allowed to inhibit research interests, teaching may become sterile and both the students and the nation become the losers. The students may fail to get the education they might have had, and the nation to get the well-educated talent it might have had.

The problem has sweeping consequences, for it is in the liberal arts college, or in the undergraduate college of a more complex institution, that most students receive the essential elements of their college education. Some graduates of colleges that do not encourage research will nevertheless become scientists. But to do so, they must rise above the shortcomings of their undergraduate years; how many potential scientists are trapped and unable to rise above their undergraduate handicaps nobody knows. The much larger number of graduates who become businessmen, teachers, lawyers, and members of other

263

professions will have had no contact with science as a quest for new knowledge, and will have but little basis for understanding the nature of science and research, the relations between basic research and human welfare, or the attitudes and conditions that best foster research.

Yet there are, of course, exceptions; President Gould himself was able to say that his own faculty included the world's foremost authority on Antarctic petrography. The existence of some exceptions demonstrates that there could be more.

If the nation is looking for ways in which to improve the education of future scientists and to provide future members of other professions with a better understanding of science—and both are vitally important educational problems—some of the best opportunities for further improvement are to be found in liberal arts colleges. The liberal arts colleges are as hard pressed for money as are the universities, and find it more difficult to secure research grants. Yet unless there are opportunities for research, a faculty of the highest quality cannot be secured.

Arrangements in Support
of Basic Research

The best arrangements for the support of basic research are those which most effectively free creative scholarship from its limitations. The limitations vary, depending upon what the scientist wants to do. But if he is a truly creative research scholar, it is worth a great deal of effort to find out what he needs, to remove whatever barriers stand in his way, and to give him positive encouragement to go ahead.

What a scientist needs depends upon the problem upon which he is working. Darwin needed the voyage of the *Beagle*. Einstein needed paper and pencil. Faraday and Henry needed some simple bits of wire and metal, and Mendel needed a garden. The needs of contemporary scientists are equally varied, and sometimes much more costly. The modern need may be for a particle accelerator costing many millions of dollars, an oceanographic research vessel, a carefully controlled environment for biological studies, or for peace and freedom to think.

What the scientist needs is not always what the donor or supporting agency wants to provide. In fact, what the donors are willing to provide may be quite inappropriate, for their thinking sometimes lags behind new scientific ideas, and often, rather curiously, lags behind the practical realities of the moment. They know what has been done, but usually not what is just beginning to be thought about. They may be prejudiced against forms of support that were not very practical some time ago, but that have now become critically necessary.

But it is the donors and supporting agencies who have the money that can be used to remove the limitations. This fact puts the scientist under temptation to do the kind of work, or to describe his plans in the terms, that will appeal to some available source of funds. No one knows how much distortion of research plans has actually resulted, but even if there has been no deliberate distortion, at very best there has been a too early freezing of plans in order to permit a scientist to describe a project in sufficient detail to secure a grant. And frequently the processes and delays of securing financial support have been a distraction from the main business of research.

A number of participants pointed out that it is particularly difficult to secure support for work in new fields. Yet it is precisely in new fields that important new knowledge is most likely to be developed. In 1895, Wilhelm Röntgen, in seven highly productive weeks, less than the time it now takes to negotiate a research contract, discovered x rays and so exhaustively studied their properties that little basic knowledge was added for 17 years. This and similar items from the history of science led several participants to play the speculative game "What

265

would have happened if?" What would have happened if Röntgen had had to secure a foundation grant to support his work? In the first place, he would have been unable to describe clearly what he was setting out to do, for he did not know. His necessarily indefinite proposal would have been referred to a panel of reviewers, and an inappropriate panel at that, for there was no panel on x rays. The reviewers would have done a conscientious job, and quite possibly they would have decided that Röntgen was a good enough man to be supported in whatever research he considered worth doing. On the other hand, the proposal might well have been rejected, for the reviewers would also have been considering proposals that were closer to their own scientific interests and that seemed likely to meet some of the apparent needs of contemporary science.

Committees stress the traditional and already known fields of research. They have to. But the most advanced and creative scholars are out in front of the traditional fields, exploring the borders of the still unknown. There are not many such pioneers, but they have an importance out of all proportion to their number.

The Key Is Creative Men

The one completely indispensable element in basic research is a scientist with an idea. He can be helped by the equipment and services that money will buy but he can never be replaced. In James Fisk's words, "basic new scientific ideas come from individual scientists and not from 'manpower.'"

The large amount of agreement with this point of view laid the basis for vigorous discussion of Merle Tuve's proposal that "we should make it clear to Congress and to the public that the whole basic record of scientific progress has been made by individual men who could spend their time freely on the scientific problems which puzzled them. I see no valid reason for not insisting that the sound support of basic research requires us to use the technique long used in the universities and copied by the private research institutes, namely, that of buying a creative man's time and giving it back to him. . . . I mean thus to say that we might use public funds to purchase a creative investigator's working lifetime, and then give it back to him to spend in his research efforts. A single lump sum of, say, $700,000 would pay the remaining lifetime salary of a gifted research man after he has been clearly identified as a creative investigator by the age of 30 or 35, and would pay in addition for one or two technical assistants or two or three students to work with him. . . . If we were to allocate 40 to 60 million dollars per year to the creation of such Research Professors or Research Scholars . . . in one decade we would have in this country a solid phalanx of 500 or 600 outstanding investigators dedicated to basic research and unquestionably free to devote their personal time and attention to creative ideas for the rest of their lives."

Difficulties with this proposal are easy to see: the administrative uncertainties of selecting the career investigators; the financial complications of finding the money; the philosophical concerns that grow out of the fact that this is only one way of forwarding basic research and in some cases is not the most effective way. But there are precedents that have worked well; the research professor at a university and the permanent staff member of a private research institution were models for Dr. Tuve's proposal. Citing a number of famous scientists as evidence, Robert Morison drew the generalization that a secure academic position and freedom to investigate whatever problems a scientist finds most challenging are conducive to research success. In the same vein, Conrad Elvehjem concluded that the research professorship "is an ideal method of insuring substantial returns for each research dollar spent, and I believe we must take steps to have the practice more generally adopted."

For the man who is really qualified for such an appointment, this, surely, is a more effective method of using talent than is the method of requiring him to hunt around for a new grant for each new idea. Confidence and trust are required, and some of the career appointees will turn out to be disappointments. But the ones who are not disappointments will be able to concentrate on research and not on getting money for each new problem. Extra funds will sometimes be needed, for some of the lifetime investigators will turn up ideas that require expensive equipment, but special grants can always be used to supplement the resources of the lifetime appointment when extra money is necessary.

The career investigatorship, or research professorship, is a means of furthering basic research that the symposium participants recommend be used more widely.

Support for Universities

The system recommended by Dr. Tuve is designed to give outstanding research scholars freedom to work uninterruptedly on what seem to them the most important scientific tasks. This is fine, for a relatively small number of outstanding scholars. But the freedom and flexibility of support that are essential for their work are also—though perhaps to a lesser extent and in modified form—important for the furtherance of all basic research. In the universities, the way to support all competent scientists is to improve and support the universities.

Support of universities contrasts sharply with the system of individual project grants, a system that came in for much and varied criticism. The project grant is made for a limited time, frequently for too short a time. It is awarded to support work that the researcher can describe in some detail, frequently too early in the course of the work to permit him to give an accurate description of what will turn out to be most worth doing. The project method of support handicaps the scholar who wants freedom to explore a new area.

These characteristics of project grants are by no means altogether bad or disadvantageous. The author of such a research proposal must think and plan in advance what it is that he intends to do. His proposal must survive the scrutiny of informed and critical scientists from other institutions. Undoubtedly this process eliminates the trivial and the more poorly conceived research proposals. The risk is that it also eliminates the newer and more imaginative ones. And the certainty is that it costs everyone involved a great deal of time. There is a tremendous overhead of proposal writing, panel meetings, conferences, discussions, and decisions in selecting the projects which can be supported by a limited research budget.

The vigorous criticism of project grants by symposium participants was made with full realization of two facts that place them in a better light than the criticisms would indicate. First, since World War II, project grants have constituted a major and an effective method of financing a large amount of research. Second, the administrators of federal scientific agencies are aware of the shortcomings of project grants, and are working to reduce the difficulties and to develop other, longer-term, and less specific means of supporting research.

University Funds

Nevertheless, dissatisfaction remains, and quite naturally there were a number of suggestions that it would be better to support universities or departments as a whole than to support individual research projects. These proposals have merit, but before this kind of support can be widely adopted, the persons responsible for making block or unrestricted grants to departments or institutions must learn how to meet the practical difficulties and pressures that they will inevitably encounter.

Under the usual method of making project grants, a foundation officer can always defend the allocation of funds on the grounds that each individual project was judged by a panel of qualified scientists and that the funds were allotted on the basis of the individual merits of the projects reviewed. If unrestricted funds were granted to departments or institutions, it would be more obvious, but not necessarily more true, that the funds were being allotted in the hope and with the faith that they would be used wisely and constructively. The administrator, however, would not have the defense that he now has of project grants, and would have to be prepared to face the pressures of college presidents and faculties, congressmen, business associates, and other supporters of disappointed applicants. This is a serious practical difficulty, but it would nevertheless be advantageous for universities to have larger amounts of unrestricted money. For there has been repeated testimony that unrestricted funds give more flexibility and continued strength than does an equal amount of project money.

In order to give wide support to university scientists, in order to free their creative scholarship from limitations, the symposium discussion again and again emphasized this principle: *Universities must always be expected to perform the largest share of basic research. In order to expand their research activities, universities must have larger amounts of unrestricted money.*

Even if the universities were as well financed as the symposium would like to see them, special grants would still sometimes be necessary. Research in some fields calls for such costly equipment that no university by itself can pay the bill. President Eisenhower gave an example in announcing to the participants plans for federal financing of a two-mile-long particle accelerator expected to cost more than $100 million to construct and some $15 million a year to operate.

Special grants and contracts can appropriately be used

for special purposes. But the Wilhelm Röntgens of the future should not have to apply for research grants to support their pioneering ventures.

The Sources of Money

Symposium participants had several things to say about the financial support of basic research. Most fundamental was the insistence that neither the federal government nor any other external agency could safely be the sole or even the primary source of research support. Universities, like individual research investigators, profit from the financial independence that enables them to pursue the research ideas that look most promising. University faculty members and officers need the financial stability as well as the moral courage that enables them to say "no" to an unwanted grant or contract.

If universities are to be able to support a greater share of basic research from their own funds, obviously they need more money under their own direct control. For while many universities now have very much larger research budgets than they had prior to World War II, they have relatively less unrestricted money than in earlier years. There was repeated insistence that out of the present federal research and development budget a larger fraction should be assigned to basic research and should be made available to the universities on an unrestricted basis. The papers by Allen Astin and James Killian were most explicit on this point.

Government Control

One of the deeply entrenched attitudes toward federal support of education is that federal support is dangerously likely to lead to federal control. But in contrast, most of the symposium participants were not worried about dangers of federal control of research supported by government funds. In fact, there was testimony to the enlightened attitude on the part of the government in seeking to avoid this danger. A political scientist among the participants pointed out that the United States Government was the one major government that was simultaneously increasing its support and decreasing its control of research and education.

The concern expressed over the small fraction of the total research and development budget going into basic research, the suggestions for improving grant procedures, and the worries about restrictions on new fields imposed by the processes of committee review were all addressed to details of practice rather than to points of fundamental principle. If the practices are improved, most participants did not seem to fear that large government support would lead to control or domination.

Full Costs of Sponsored Research

The federal government as a source of research funds was the target of the frequently repeated charge that many government grants and contracts do not pay full costs. There was no argument; representatives of the federal agencies that support research and representatives of the universities that receive the support all agreed on this point. The problem is serious because the total amount of money coming from federal grants and contracts is large; in a few universities the total value of grants and contracts is so large that the indirect or overhead costs alone run to several million dollars a year. The result, as Lee DuBridge vigorously described it, is that the universities which do the most research are in the difficult and morally dubious position of having to appeal to industry, to alumni, and to other friends to secure unrestricted gifts with which to make up the difference. What cannot be made up by gifts comes out of faculty salaries.

272

It is probably impossible to estimate the extent to which research progress has been retarded by the failure of government to pay full costs of the research it chooses to support. But that the failure has produced irritation, has robbed scientists of time better spent on research, and has forced university administrators to beg, borrow, and scrimp to make up the difference is sufficient justification for changing government practice. The overhead which would be necessary to accomplish this very important purpose is, in fact, modest as compared with the overhead which is regularly paid by government on commercial development contracts.

Research under Government Contracts

One of the problems faced by industrial companies holding large government contracts has been the difficulty of securing reimbursement for the costs of basic research. On a government contract, particularly a cost-reimbursable contract, government auditors have, quite understandably, sought to exclude from the list of reimbursable items anything that could not be directly related to the object of the contract. Thus equipment, salaries, or building maintenance have been accepted as necessary for the fulfillment of the contract. But maintenance of the quality of the scientific staff through engagement in basic research has frequently been ruled out.

A company in this predicament has two options. If it chooses to engage in little or no basic research, it risks the loss of some of its abler scientists and it runs the danger of falling behind competitors in its ability to secure contracts for work that involves advanced technology and new scientific ideas.

Alternatively, if the company does engage in basic research in an effort to avoid the above dangers, it must pay the cost of that research out of profits instead of having those costs reimbursed under its government contracts. The attitude of directors and stockholders toward reduced profits requires no comment.

It seems to be clearly in the national interest for the federal government to help its major contractors to keep in the forefront of an advancing science and technology. Discussions between industrial and government (primarily Department of Defense) representatives should lead to a solution of this problem.

Possible Changes in Federal Taxes

Colleges and universities need unrestricted funds, and as one source of such funds they are relying increasingly on gifts from alumni, parents of students, industrial friends, and other supporters, both private and corporate. The proposal introduced by Paul Klopsteg and endorsed by a number of other participants is designed to produce a substantial increase in the volume of these gifts. The gist of the suggestion is that the internal revenue code be amended to permit both private and corporate gifts to institutions of higher education to be treated as credits against income tax instead of as deductions in computing adjusted gross income. The amount of credit would be limited to a percentage of adjusted gross income, but the credit itself would be so handled as to equalize the out-of-pocket costs to taxpayers of high and low income for each dollar they give to institutions of higher education.

At present it costs a person in the highest income tax bracket only 9 cents to make a one-dollar gift to a university or college, while it costs a person in the lowest tax bracket 80 cents to make a one-dollar gift. This difference results from the 91 per cent and 20 per cent tax rates for the highest and lowest taxable income groups. The incentive to make such gifts is clearly greater for the man in the high tax bracket, and such men do make larger gifts, in proportion to income, than do those in the lower brackets.

But the number of persons in the income range of, say, $5,000 to $50,000 a year is much larger than the number in the higher ranges, and so is their collective income. With proper incentive, their potential contribution to higher education would be greater than it now is and greater than the contribution of the much smaller number of wealthy men. Since this income range includes most of the people who have a serious continuing interest in the improvement of higher education, making it more attractive for them to donate money to colleges and universities would be expected to increase substantially the flow of unrestricted funds that the symposium considered to be most urgent. Broadening the base of support would also have the great advantage of providing a statistically more stable flow of support.

Dr. Klopsteg would make giving more attractive by offering to all persons in all income brackets the opportunity to reduce their income tax payments by 91 per cent of the amount (up to 15 per cent of adjusted gross income) given to institutions of higher education.

This proposal elicited more questions from the audience than did any other suggestion for improving the support of basic research. It merits widespread consideration, for it holds promise of achieving the increase in unrestricted funds that the universities must have if they are to continue to fulfill their highest functions.

Industrial Support

Corporate gifts to higher education and the most effective methods of industrial support are matters to which industry has been giving growing attention. Robert Wilson cited the favorable experience of the petroleum industry in its cooperative support of university research. A number of the industrial participants spoke of the growing support their companies have been giving to universities. And President Eisenhower emphasized the importance of industrial support as a means of avoiding a dangerously great dependence of universities on federal financing.

The responsibility of industry to conduct basic research in its own laboratories was also considered. Robert Wilson generalized that the more experience an industry had with research, the greater the emphasis it placed on basic research. If this generalization remains true, the future will see increased industrial commitment to basic research. There was a strong feeling, however, that this trend should be accelerated. Exact figures will vary, but no one challenged Robert Oppenheimer's suggestion that, in general, from one sixth to one fifth of the time of the research staff might profitably be devoted to work not directly related to the company's immediate production problems. Among others, Allen Astin contended that an applied-research laboratory will attract and hold higher quality personnel if some such fraction of the time is recognized as appropriately devoted to basic research.

The Private Foundations

Recent reports by the National Science Foundation and the President's Science Advisory Committee have suggested that the private foundations have special opportunities for supporting pioneering and more imaginative research, since the federal government cannot be as venturesome or imaginative as can the private foundations. Robert Morison examined this position quite explicitly, and replied that some government agencies are so well financed that they are in a better position than the private foundations to take risks on bright new ideas brought in by untried investigators.

276

But suppose that the private foundations do have "a vital and unique role," as the President's Science Advisory Committee says, "in supporting imaginative and audacious research that industry or Government may not always support." There are some puzzling implications. The foundations control only a very small fraction of the total money available for research support. As government and industrial funds grow larger and larger, the foundations are quite likely—indeed some of them feel impelled—to follow their historic role of pace setters by transferring their support from the physical and biological sciences to the social sciences and humanities. Does this leave the most imaginative research in the natural sciences with no source of support? Government agencies cannot blandly leave to private foundations the double responsibility of pioneering new fields and supporting all the bolder and more risky ventures in the old fields. The foundations simply do not have enough money to run the risks in all fields.

This particular puzzle went unresolved, but the discussion made it clear that the private foundations have in the past played a uniquely effective role in recognizing the importance of new fields and in supporting pioneering research with a flexibility and boldness that government agencies and many universities could not match. The continuing importance of such support was pointed out again and again during the symposium discussion.

Communication

It has long been recognized that the progress of basic research is vitally dependent on the freedom and effectiveness of communication among scientists. Symposium participants did not have a great deal to say about this problem, partly because it was taken for granted that the present major efforts to improve communication would be continued. But several points were

277

reaffirmed. The prompt publication of research findings is highly desirable, as are improved facilities for abstracting, translating, and retrieving published material. Freedom of communication, through publication, travel, and international scientific meetings is beneficial to all scientists, but most beneficial to those from the scientifically more advanced countries, for they have the knowledge and facilities that will enable them to make best use of new ideas and information. Attempts to withhold basic scientific information from other scientists are usually self-defeating. Security classification, which may properly be imposed on technological developments and plans for military use, is out of place and of little effect in withholding basic scientific knowledge from other countries, and is likely to do more harm than good to the country that thinks it can keep basic knowledge secret.

General Principles and Specific Laboratories

The recommendations and suggestions of the symposium discussion were general, intended for the nation as a whole, its government, its institutions of higher education, its industrial companies, and its scientists. Much work will be necessary to bring about the proposed changes, but the goals justify much work.

In the meantime, there is opportunity for an individual university, or for an individual research laboratory—in industry, in government, or in a private foundation—to put into effect as many of the improvements as it can manage and as apply to its case. The climate of an individual laboratory and its own individual arrangements in support of basic research have a direct and immediate influence upon every scientist on the staff.

Allen Astin's remarks about government laboratories apply to all research laboratories: "No laboratory can maintain productivity in research without high-quality personnel. No laboratory can retain first-rate personnel without permitting the right and freedom of basic questioning. . . . No scientist of quality would remain where the frontiers of science are closed to him." Each laboratory director is responsible for the arrangements and the intellectual climate of his own laboratory. What he does determines the quality of the staff and of their work.

Promotion of Excellence

Basic research is a product of able, trained, supported, free scholars. Such scholars and such research are found in industrial, government, and private laboratories, but it is the universities that have evolved as the institutions with the greatest responsibility to produce such scholars and to assist their endeavors. One of the most certain ways in which society can promote excellence in science and other areas of scholarship is by building strong universities and insisting that creative scholars be given time, facilities, and freedom of choice to carry out the studies that seem most likely to extend fundamental knowledge and understanding.

Clearly a basic requisite is that the universities have sufficient unrestricted money to be able to carry out at a level of high effectiveness their continuing responsibilities of teaching and creative scholarship. With such funds, the university can be trusted to maintain a fair balance between teaching and research and among the various fields of scholarship. With such funds, it can attract and hold an able staff, who will attract and educate able students.

Within the faculty, however, there will inevitably be some men of greater competence than others. There will be some who need more expensive facilities than others. A university can recognize these differences, but it cannot adjust to their full range. Some men deserve a kind and level of support that cannot be defended from the university's internal point of view, for only by depriving many colleagues of what is due them

279

could such support be given. But an outside agency can step in and provide this kind of support when it is merited, and can do so without diminishing the support that goes to other members of the faculty. In fact, the other members will welcome the distinction and assistance that has come to their colleague, for such support, especially from an agency that is national or international in scope, adds luster to the institution as a whole, and raises the sights of the university and the community as to the kind of support that is reasonable and necessary if the nation is to have the most productive program of basic research.

Acknowledgments

The preparation of this summary would have been impossible without the help of a rapporteur for each of the first four sessions and two rapporteurs for the final day of discussion. Each recorded and analyzed the discussion during the session for which he was responsible. Working together after the conclusion of the symposium, they provided a full and excellent account of what had gone on—the agreements and disagreements, the points of emphasis, the conclusions, the questions that were answered, and the ones that went unresolved. Their records, together with the formal papers, provided the basis for this summary chapter. The rapporteurs were:

Mary I. Bunting, Dean, Douglass College, Rutgers University
Graham P. DuShane, Editor, *Science*
Gerald Holton, Professor of Physics, Harvard University
Harry C. Kelly, Assistant Director for Scientific Personnel and Education, National Science Foundation
Walter A. Rosenblith, Professor of Communications Biophysics, Department of Electrical Engineering, Massachusetts Institute of Technology
Douglas Whitaker, Vice President for Administration, Rockefeller Institute

They and members of the committee that planned the symposium have generously and thoughtfully criticized earlier drafts of this summary. Their criticisms have made it a clearer and more accurate account of the thinking of the symposium participants.

PARTICIPANTS

Note. A dagger indicates guests who attended only Session III on May 14, 1959. An asterisk indicates participants in discussion session on May 16, 1959.

† Frank W. Abrams
    Trustee, Alfred P. Sloan Foundation
† Ruth Abramson
    Sloan-Kettering Institute for Cancer Research
† Charles F. Adams
    President, Raytheon Manufacturing Company
  Roger Adams
    Emeritus Professor of Chemistry, University of Illinois
  John N. Adkins
    Deputy Science Director, Office of Naval Research
† Willcox B. Adsit
    Vice President, General Motors Acceptance Corporation
  A. Adrian Albert
    Professor of Mathematics, University of Chicago
† George E. Allen
    Board Member, Republic Steel Corporation
  H. Julian Allen
    Chief, High Speed Research Division, Ames Research Center, Moffatt Field, California (National Aeronautics and Space Administration)
† Joseph Allen
    Alfred P. Sloan Foundation
† Sidney Allen
    Vice President, Mutual Broadcasting System, Inc.
  Harry Alpert
    Dean, Graduate School, University of Oregon

PARTICIPANTS

† V. D. Angerman
        Publisher, *Science and Mechanics*

  Fontaine C. Armistead
        Director, Virginia Institute for Scientific Research   . . . .

* Richard T. Arnold
        Program Administrator, Basic Physical Sciences, Alfred P. Sloan Foundation

* Allen V. Astin
        Director, National Bureau of Standards

† C. J. Backstrand
        President, Armstrong Cork Company

† C. Everett Bacon
        Spencer Trask and Company

* William O. Baker
        Vice President, Research, Bell Telephone Laboratories

† Glenn P. Bakken
        President, Chase Brass and Copper Company

† Rudolph F. Bannow
        National Vice President, National Association of Manufacturers

† Joseph W. Barker
        Director, Research Corporation

† Fred W. Bartlett
        Chairman of the Board, Socony Mobil Oil Company, Inc.

† Bruce Barton
        Chairman of the Board, Batten, Barton, Durstine and Osborn, Inc.

  Henry A. Barton
        Associate Director, American Institute of Physics

† Clarence W. Bartow
        Drexel and Company

* Stanhope Bayne-Jones
        Former Dean, Yale University School of Medicine (Washington, D. C.)

† Stewart Beach
        Executive Editor, *This Week Magazine*

* George W. Beadle
        Chairman, Division of Biology, California Institute of Technology

282

† Arnold O. Beckman
  President, Beckman Instruments, Inc.
† Elliott V. Bell
  Chairman of the Executive Committee, McGraw-Hill Publishing Company, Inc.
  Welcome W. Bender
  Director, RIAS
* H. Stanley Bennett
  Chairman, Department of Anatomy, University of Washington
  Ralph D. Bennett
  Manager, General Electric Vallecitos Atomic Laboratory
* Lloyd V. Berkner
  President, Associated Universities, Inc.
† Joseph M. Bertotti
  Manager, Educational Relations, General Electric Company
  David H. Blackwell
  Professor of Statistics, University of California
† A. Harold Blatt
  Professor of Chemistry, Queens College
† Oscar Bodansky
  Professor of Biochemistry, Sloan-Kettering Institute for Cancer Research
  James F. Bonner
  Professor of Biology, California Institute of Technology
  Carl W. Borgmann
  Director, Program in Science and Engineering, Ford Foundation
* James F. Bourland
  General Manager, Central Research Division, American Cyanamid Company
† Edward W. Bourne
  Alexander and Green
† Marion W. Boyer
  Director, Standard Oil Company (New Jersey)
* Richard Bradfield
  Professor of Soil Technology, Cornell University

283

PARTICIPANTS

* ALBERT BRADLEY
          Chairman of the Board, Alfred P. Sloan Foundation

HERMAN R. BRANSON
          Chairman, Department of Physics, Howard University

* A. CALVIN BRATTON
          Director of Pharmacological Research, Parke, Davis and
          Company

† MABEL H. BRIGHT
          Rockefeller Institute

ROBERT B. BRODE
          Associate Director, National Science Foundation

* DETLEV W. BRONK
          President, Rockefeller Institute

† CECIL L. BROWN
          Manager of Scientific Research, Esso Research and Engi-
          neering Company

† GEORGE B. BROWN
          Professor of Biochemistry, Sloan-Kettering Division of Cor-
          nell University Medical College

YALE BROZEN
          Professor of Economics, University of Chicago

† JOHN C. BUGHER
          Consultant on Nuclear Energy Affairs, Rockefeller Founda-
          tion

† HOWARD S. BUNN
          President, Union Carbide Corporation

* MARY I. BUNTING
          Dean, Douglass College, Rutgers University

† EDWIN S. BURDELL
          President, Cooper Union for the Advancement of Science
          and Art

† CARTER L. BURGESS
          President, American Machine and Foundry Company

† WILLIAM H. BURKHART
          Chairman of the Board, Lever Brothers Company

PAUL R. BURKHOLDER
          Director of Research, Brooklyn Botanic Garden

* T. C. BYERLY
>   Deputy Administrator, Agricultural Research Service, U. S. Department of Agriculture

ROBERT W. CAIRNS
>   Director of Research, Hercules Powder Company

† ROBERT D. CALKINS
>   President, Brookings Institution

JOHN M. CAMPBELL
>   Scientific Director, General Motors Corporation

R. KEITH CANNAN
>   Chairman, Division of Medical Sciences, National Academy of Sciences—National Research Council

WILLIAM D. CAREY
>   Executive Assistant to the Director, Bureau of the Budget

* THOMAS P. CARNEY
>   Vice President, Research, Development and Control, Eli Lilly and Company

WALTER S. CARPENTER, JR.
>   Chairman, E. I. du Pont de Nemours and Company

* BRITTON CHANCE
>   Johnson Professor of Biophysics, University of Pennsylvania

† ALBERT K. CHAPMAN
>   President, Eastman Kodak Company

* CARL J. CHRISTENSEN
>   Director, Utah Engineering Experiment Station, University of Utah

J. KAPP CLARK
>   Director of Research, Smith, Kline and French Laboratories

† LUCIUS D. CLAY
>   Chairman of the Board, Continental Can Company, Inc.

LOWELL T. COGGESHALL
>   Dean, Division of the Biological Sciences, University of Chicago

† LESTER L. COLBERT
>   President, Chrysler Corporation

† CHARLES W. COLE
>   President, Amherst College

PARTICIPANTS

JOHN S. COLEMAN
> Executive Secretary, Division of Physical Sciences, National Academy of Sciences—National Research Council

† MYRON A. COLER
> President, Markite Corporation

JAMES S. COLES
> President, Bowdoin College

† JOHN L. COLLYER
> Chairman of the Board, B. F. Goodrich Company

† S. SLOAN COLT
> Director, Bankers Trust Company

† JAMES COMERFORD
> President, Consolidated Natural Gas Company

† J. R. COMINSKY
> Publisher, *The Saturday Review*

* BARRY COMMONER
> Professor of Plant Physiology, Washington University

* EDWARD U. CONDON
> Chairman, Department of Physics, Washington University

† ALFRED D. COOK
> Editor, *Electronic News*

† REGINALD G. COOMBE
> Chairman of the Board, Memorial Center for Cancer and Allied Diseases, and Trustee, Sloan-Kettering Institute for Cancer Research

* ARTHUR C. COPE
> Chairman, Department of Chemistry, Massachusetts Institute of Technology

GEORGE W. CORNER
> Historian, Rockefeller Institute

† PHILIP CORTNEY
> President, Coty, Inc.

† H. P. CORWITH
> Vice President, Western Union Telegraph Company

* CORNELIUS P. COTTER
> Executive Director, Republican Committee on Program and Progress

286

† Richard Courant
        Professor of Mathematics, New York University

† Euclid M. Covington
        President, *This Week Magazine*

† John Cowles
        President, *The Minneapolis Star and Tribune*

† Hiden T. Cox
        Executive Director, American Institute of Biological Sciences

Frank Croxton
        Technical Director, Battelle Memorial Institute

† Harlow H. Curtice
        Director, General Motors Corporation

† Helena Curtis
        Sloan-Kettering Institute for Cancer Research

John H. Curtiss
        Executive Director, American Mathematical Society

Gilbert Dalldorf
        Consultant to the National Foundation

† John Charles Daly
        Vice President, American Broadcasting Company

† Charles A. Dana
        Chairman of the Board, Dana Corporation

Farrington Daniels
        Chairman, Department of Chemistry, University of Wisconsin

† Donald K. David
        Chairman of the Board, Committee for Economic Development

† Watson Davis
        Director, Science Service

† Emerson Day
        Chief, Division of Preventive Medicine, Sloan-Kettering Institute for Cancer Research

† William C. Decker
        President, Corning Glass Works

Milislav Demerec
        Head, Department of Genetics, Carnegie Institution of Washington (Cold Spring Harbor)

287

MAJOR GENERAL MARVIN C. DEMLER
  Director of Research and Development, U. S. Air Force

* EDWARD W. DEMPSEY
  Head, Department of Anatomy, Washington University

† ARTHUR R. T. DENUES
  Deputy Director, Sloan-Kettering Institute for Cancer Research

† THOMAS E. DEWEY
  Dewey, Ballantine, Bushby, Palmer and Wood

* JOHN S. DICKEY
  President, Dartmouth College

† ARTHUR O. DIETZ
  President, CIT Financial Corporation

KARL DITTMER
  Program Administrator, American Chemical Society Petroleum Research Fund

THEODOSIUS DOBZHANSKY
  Professor of Zoology, Columbia University

PAUL M. DOTY
  Professor of Chemistry, Harvard University

† WILLIAM J. DRISCOLL
  Vice President, Chemical Corn Exchange Bank

* HUGH L. DRYDEN
  Deputy Administrator, National Aeronautics and Space Administration

RENÉ J. DUBOS
  Member, Rockefeller Institute

* LEE A. DuBRIDGE
  President, California Institute of Technology

CHARLES L. DUNHAM
  Director, Division of Biology and Medicine, U. S. Atomic Energy Commission

† JOHN R. DUNNING
  Dean, School of Engineering, Columbia University

* GRAHAM P. DuSHANE
  Editor, *Science*

Vincent duVigneaud
> Head, Department of Biochemistry, Cornell University Medical School

† Ira C. Eaker
> Vice President, Douglas Aircraft Company, Inc.

† Ferdinand Eberstadt
> F. Eberstadt and Company

Robert H. Ebert
> Director of Medicine, University Hospitals of Cleveland

John T. Edsall
> Professor of Biochemistry, Harvard University

† Dwight D. Eisenhower
> President of the United States

† Major John S. Eisenhower
> United States Army

† Donald M. Elliman
> President, Bank of New York

* Conrad A. Elvehjem
> President, University of Wisconsin

* Elmer W. Engstrom
> Senior Executive Vice President, Radio Corporation of America

Robert C. Ernst
> Dean, Speed Scientific School, University of Louisville

John C. Evvard
> Assistant Director, Lewis Research Center, Cleveland (National Aeronautics and Space Administration)

* Larkin H. Farinholt
> Deputy Science Adviser, Department of State

† Michael Ference, Jr.
> Director of Scientific Laboratory, Ford Motor Company

† Roy K. Ferguson
> Chairman of the Board, St. Regis Paper Company

Harold E. Finley
> Chairman, Department of Zoology, Howard University

* James B. Fisk
> President, Bell Telephone Laboratories

† Dennis Flanagan
    Editor, *Scientific American*

Charles L. Fleming, Jr.
    Director, Products Research Division, Esso Research and Engineering Company

* Paul J. Flory
    Executive Director for Research, Mellon Institute

† Henry C. Flower, Jr.
    Vice Chairman, J. Walter Thompson Company

† Francis M. Flynn
    President, *New York Daily News*

Karl A. Folkers
    Executive Director, Fundamental Research, Merck and Company, Inc.

Sidney W. Fox
    Director, Oceanographic Institute, Florida State University

Thomas Francis, Jr.
    Chairman, Department of Epidemiology, School of Public Health, University of Michigan

Joseph S. Fruton
    Chairman, Department of Biochemistry, Yale University

† Hon. James G. Fulton
    Congressman from Pennsylvania

† G. Keith Funston
    President, New York Stock Exchange

Clifford C. Furnas
    Chancellor, University of Buffalo

† Buell G. Gallagher
    President, City College

† Harold J. Gallagher
    Willkie, Farr, Gallagher, Walton and Fitz Gibbon

† Thomas F. Gallagher
    Chief, Division of Steroid Metabolism and Biochemistry, Sloan-Kettering Institute for Cancer Research

Ralph W. Gerard
    Professor of Neurophysiology, Mental Health Research Institute, University of Michigan

* Ivan A. Getting
>   Vice President for Engineering and Research, Raytheon Manufacturing Company

† Carl J. Gilbert
>   Chairman, Gillette Company

† S. Hazard Gillespie, Jr.
>   Davis, Polk, Wardwell, Sunderland and Kiendl

† Louis C. Goad
>   Executive Vice President, General Motors Corporation

* David R. Goddard
>   Chairman, Department of Botany, University of Pennsylvania

Martin Goland
>   Director, Southwest Research Institute

† John F. Gordon
>   President, General Motors Corporation

† Charles L. Gould
>   Assistant Publisher, *New York Journal American*

* Laurence M. Gould
>   President, Carleton College

† Joseph A. Grazier
>   President, American Radiator and Standard Sanitary Corporation

Estill I. Green
>   Vice President, Bell Telephone Laboratories

† Crawford H. Greenwalt
>   President, E. I. du Pont de Nemours & Company

† Mason W. Gross
>   President, Rutgers University

* Paul M. Gross
>   Vice President, Duke University

Harry Grundfest
>   Associate Professor of Neurology, College of Physicians and Surgeons, Columbia University

† William P. Gwinn
>   President, United Aircraft Corporation

PARTICIPANTS

* LAWRENCE R. HAFSTAD
     Vice President and Director, Research Staff, General Motors Corporation
† JAMES C. HAGERTY
     Press Secretary to the President
  RALPH S. HALFORD
     Professor of Chemistry, Columbia University
† DONALD R. HAMILTON
     Dean of the Graduate School, Princeton University
* LOUIS P. HAMMETT
     Professor of Chemistry, Columbia University
† JOHNSON F. HAMMOND
     Editor, *Journal of the American Medical Association*
* J. GEORGE HARRAR
     Director for Agriculture, Division of Natural Sciences and Agriculture, Rockefeller Foundation
† HENRY B. HASS
     President, Sugar Research Foundation, Inc.
* LELAND J. HAWORTH
     Director, Brookhaven National Laboratory
† IRWIN HERSEY
     Editor, *Astronautics*
  SEYMOUR W. HERWALD
     Vice President, Research, Westinghouse Electric Corporation
† REV. THEODORE M. HESBURGH
     President, University of Notre Dame
† HENRY H. HEWETSON
     Vice President, Standard Oil Company (New Jersey)
* JULIAN W. HILL
     Executive Secretary, Committee on Educational Aid, E. I. du Pont de Nemours & Company
* JAMES HILLIER
     General Manager, Radio Corporation of America Laboratories
* J. WILLIAM HINKLEY
     President and Director, Research Corporation
* JOSEPH C. HINSEY
     Director, New York Hospital-Cornell Medical Center

292

E. S. Hiscocks
> Director, United Kingdom Scientific Mission

* Alexander Hollaender
> Director, Biological Division, Oak Ridge National Laboratory

* Gerald Holton
> Professor of Physics, Harvard University

† R. Karl Honaman
> Director of Publications, Bell Telephone Laboratories, Inc.

Frank L. Horsfall, Jr.
> Vice President for Clinical Studies and Physician-in-Chief, Rockefeller Institute

* William V. Houston
> President, Rice Institute

* Frank A. Howard
> President, Sloan-Kettering Institute for Cancer Research

† Jack R. Howard
> President, Scripps-Howard Newspapers

† Roy W. Howard
> Chairman, Executive Committee, Scripps-Howard Newspapers

John A. Hrones
> Vice President for Academic Affairs, Case Institute of Technology

Joseph D. Hughes
> Vice President, T. Mellon and Sons

† George M. Humphrey
> Chairman, National Steel Corporation

† Joel Hunter
> President, Crucible Steel Company of America

Robert D. Huntoon
> Deputy Director, National Bureau of Standards

† Roy T. Hurley
> Chairman and President, Curtiss-Wright Corporation

Elmer Hutchisson
> Director, American Institute of Physics

* Arthur D. Hyde
> Vice President in Charge of Research, General Mills, Inc.

PARTICIPANTS

† Joseph A. W. Iglehart
    W. E. Hutton and Company

† Harry K. Ihrig
    Vice President in Charge of Research, Allis-Chalmers Manufacturing Company

† John B. Inglis
    Price Waterhouse and Company

George W. Irving, Jr.
    Deputy Administrator, Agricultural Research Service, U. S. Department of Agriculture

† Alvin R. Jennings
    Lybrand, Ross Bros. and Montgomery

† Earl J. Johnson
    Vice President, United Press International

† Marion A. Johnson
    Dean of the Graduate School, Rutgers University

† Devereux C. Josephs
    Chairman of the Board, New York Life Insurance Company

† Rev. Edmund P. Joyce
    Executive Vice President, University of Notre Dame

† Jasper H. Kane
    Vice President in Charge of Research, Chas. Pfizer and Company, Inc.

Joseph Kaplan
    Professor of Physics, University of California

A. Richard Kassander
    Associate Professor of Physics, University of Arizona

† Stuart E. Kay
    Vice President, International Paper Company

Carl F. Kayan
    Executive Officer, Department of Mechanical Engineering, Columbia University

† Barnaby C. Keeney
    President, Brown University

† Nicholas Kelley
    Kelley, Drye, Newhall and Maginnes

CHARLES E. KELLOGG
Assistant Administrator, Soil Conservation Service, U. S. Department of Agriculture

* HARRY C. KELLY
Assistant Director for Scientific Personnel and Education, National Science Foundation

† JAMES F. KENNEY
Alfred P. Sloan Foundation

† RICHARD L. KENYON
Editor, *Chemical and Engineering News*

SEYMOUR S. KETY
Chief of Laboratory of Clinical Science, National Institute of Mental Health

† JAMES R. KILLIAN, JR.
Special Assistant to the President for Science and Technology

CHARLES N. KIMBALL
President, Midwest Research Institute

† LINDSLEY F. KIMBALL
Executive Vice President, Rockefeller Foundation

† GEORGE F. KIRBY
Vice President, Ethyl Corporation

† GRAYSON L. KIRK
President, Columbia University

* PAUL E. KLOPSTEG
President, American Association for the Advancement of Science

† ALLEN T. KLOTS
Winthrop, Stimson, Putnam and Roberts

ROBERT N. KREIDLER
Executive Secretary, Federal Council for Science and Technology

† ANDREW A. KUCHER
Vice President, Ford Motor Company

† POLYKARP KUSCH
Professor of Physics, Columbia University

* EDWIN H. LAND
President, Polaroid Corporation

295

RUDOLPH E. LANGER
>Professor of Mathematics, University of Wisconsin

†SIGURD S. LARMON
>Chairman of the Board, Young and Rubicam, Inc.

PETER D. LAX
>Associate Professor of Mathematics, New York University

* CHAUNCEY D. LEAKE
>Assistant Dean, College of Medicine, Ohio State University

MILTON O. LEE
>Secretary, Federation of American Societies for Experimental Biology

† VAN H. LEICHLITER
>President, American Steel and Wire Division, United States Steel Corporation

* SAMUEL LENHER
>Vice President, E. I. du Pont de Nemours & Company

† JOHN J. LENNON
>American Metal Climax, Inc.

† DAVID J. LEWIS
>Paine, Webber, Jackson and Curtis

CLARENCE H. LINDER
>Vice President, Engineering, General Electric Company

* FREDERICK C. LINDVALL
>Chairman, Division of Engineering, California Institute of Technology

† ROYAL LITTLE
>Chairman, Textron, Inc.

HERBERT E. LONGENECKER
>Vice President in Charge of the Chicago Professional Colleges, University of Illinois

WHEELER G. LOVELL
>Research Adviser, Ethyl Corporation

† HENRY R. LUCE
>Editor-in-Chief, *Time*, Incorporated

J. MURRAY LUCK
>Professor of Biochemistry, Stanford University

Colin M. MacLeod
> Professor of Research Medicine, University of Pennsylvania School of Medicine

† Robert E. MacNeal
> President, Curtis Publishing Company

† Harland Manchester
> Roving Editor, *Reader's Digest*

* Paul C. Mangelsdorf
> Director, Botanical Museum, Harvard University

Donald G. Marquis
> Social Science Research Council

Robert E. Marshak
> Chairman, Department of Physics, University of Rochester

William H. Martin
> Director, Research and Development, Department of the Army

O. T. Marzke
> Vice President, United States Steel Corporation

John R. Mayor
> Director of Education, American Association for the Advancement of Science

* Ernst Mayr
> Alexander Agassiz Professor of Zoology, Museum of Comparative Zoology, Harvard College

* Katharine E. McBride
> President, Bryn Mawr College

† Charles B. McCabe
> Publisher, *New York Mirror*

† James McCormack, Jr.
> Vice President, Massachusetts Institute of Technology

† V. Rev. Laurence J. McGinley
> President, Fordham University

Raymond W. McNamee
> Manager of Research Administration, Union Carbide Corporation

* William W. McPeak
> Vice President, Ford Foundation

Edward J. McShane
> Professor of Mathematics, University of Virginia

PARTICIPANTS

* ROBERT F. MEHL
    Dean of Graduate Studies, Carnegie Institute of Technology
PAUL MELLON
    Trustee, Mellon Institute
† GLENN B. MILLER
    President, Allied Chemical Corporation
NEAL E. MILLER
    James Rowland Angell Professor of Psychology, Yale University
JOHN W. MILNOR
    Associate Professor of Mathematics, Princeton University
HELEN MILTON
    Research Assistant to the Director, Operations Research Office, Johns Hopkins University
‡ HENRY ALLEN MOE
    Secretary General, John Simon Guggenheim Memorial Foundation
* DEANE MONTGOMERY
    Professor of Mathematics, Institute for Advanced Study
* MAURICE L. MOORE
    Vice President, Sterling Drug, Inc.
† MAURICE T. MOORE
    Cravath, Swaine and Moore
† ROBERT A. MOORE
    President, State University of New York, Downstate Medical Center
† MALCOLM C. MOOS
    Professor of Political Science, Johns Hopkins University
† HOWARD J. MORGENS
    President, Procter and Gamble Company
* ROBERT S. MORISON
    Director for Medical and Natural Sciences, Rockefeller Foundation
* JOSEPH C. MORRIS
    Vice President, Tulane University
† ANDREW M. MRAS
    President, American Metal Products Company

298

PARTICIPANTS

† MALCOLM MUIR
     President and Editor-in-Chief, *Newsweek*

† WALTER A. MUNNS
     President, Smith, Kline and French Laboratories

† GEORGE MURNANE, SR.
     Lazard Frères and Company

* EGER V. MURPHREE
     President, Esso Research and Engineering Company

* GEORGE M. MURPHY
     Chairman, Department of Chemistry, Washington Square College, New York University

† CLARENCE J. MYERS
     President, New York Life Insurance Company

SAMUEL M. NABRIT
     President, Texas Southern University

† GLENN A. NESTY
     Vice President, Allied Chemical Corporation

† CARROLL VINCENT NEWSOM
     President, New York University

† THOMAS S. NICHOLS
     Chairman of the Board, Olin Mathieson Chemical Corporation

† MORRIS NIELSEN
     President, Babcock and Wilcox Company

THOMAS B. NOLAN
     Director, U. S. Geological Survey

† BRIAN O'BRIEN
     Consultant, American Optical Company

CHARLES E. ODEGAARD
     President, University of Washington

BRUCE S. OLD
     Vice President, Arthur D. Little, Inc.

† IRVING S. OLDS
     White and Case

* J. ROBERT OPPENHEIMER
     Director, Institute for Advanced Study

* CHARLES G. OVERBERGER
    Head, Department of Chemistry, Polytechnic Institute of Brooklyn

† RALPH DELAHAYE PAINE, JR.
    Publisher, *Fortune*

THOMAS PARK
    Professor of Zoology, University of Chicago

† MOREHEAD PATTERSON
    Chairman, American Machine and Foundry Company

† T. F. PATTON
    President, Republic Steel Corporation

JOHN R. PAUL
    Professor of Preventive Medicine, Yale University School of Medicine

PAUL B. PEARSON
    Associate, Program in Science and Engineering, Ford Foundation

† THOMAS L. PERKINS
    Chairman of the Board, American Cyanamid Company

† ALBERT J. PHILLIPS
    Vice President and Director of Research, American Smelting and Refining Company

† GERARD PIEL
    Publisher, *Scientific American*

* EMANUEL R. PIORE
    Director of Research, International Business Machines Corporation

* JOHN D. PORTERFIELD
    Deputy Surgeon General, U. S. Public Health Service

SARWONO PRAWIROHARDJO
    President, Council for Sciences of Indonesia

† H. W. PRENTIS, JR.
    Chairman of the Board, Armstrong Cork Company

G. BALEY PRICE
    Chairman, Department of Mathematics, University of Kansas

PARTICIPANTS

* Don K. Price
>Dean, Graduate School of Public Administration, Harvard University

C. Ladd Prosser
>Professor of Physiology, University of Illinois

† John W. Queenan
>Managing Partner, Haskins and Sells

* Isidor I. Rabi
>Professor of Physics, Columbia University

† Henry T. Randall
>Clinical Director, Memorial Center for Cancer and Allied Diseases

† Roland L. Redmond
>President, Metropolitan Museum of Art

* Mina S. Rees
>Dean of Faculty, Hunter College

* Francis W. Reichelderfer
>Chief, U. S. Weather Bureau

† Orr E. Reynolds
>Director, Office of Science, Office of the Director of Defense Research and Engineering

Cornelius P. Rhoads
>Director, Sloan-Kettering Institute for Cancer Research

* Francis O. Rice
>Head, Chemistry Department, Catholic University of America

† Joseph E. Ridder
>Chairman of the Board, *The Journal of Commerce*

* Henry Riecken
>Head, Office of Social Science, National Science Foundation

* George Rieveschl
>Scientific Assistant to the President, Parke, Davis and Company

† Joseph M. Ripley
>Ivy Lee and T. J. Ross

William J. Robbins
>Emeritus Director, New York Botanical Garden

† CLIFFORD ROBERTS
>Reynolds and Company

* WALTER ORR ROBERTS
>Director, High Altitude Observatory, University of Colorado

* WILLIAM J. ROBERTS
>Director of Research, Celanese Corporation of America

* HOWARD P. ROBERTSON
>Professor of Mathematical Physics, California Institute of Technology

* RANDAL M. ROBERTSON
>Assistant Director, Division of Mathematical, Physical, and Engineering Sciences, National Science Foundation

† WILLIAM E. ROBINSON
>Chairman of the Board, Coca-Cola Company

† WILLARD F. ROCKWELL
>Chairman of the Board, Rockwell-Standard Corporation

* WALTER A. ROSENBLITH
>Professor of Communications Biophysics, Department of Electrical Engineering, Massachusetts Institute of Technology

† THOMAS J. ROSS
>Ivy Lee and T. J. Ross

† SIDNEY G. ROTH
>Coordinator of Research Services, New York University

† WILLIAM R. ROVENSKY
>Hornblower and Weeks

* WILLIAM W. RUBEY
>Research Geologist, U. S. Geological Survey

† GEORGE RUSSELL
>Executive Vice President, General Motors Corporation

JOHN M. RUSSELL
>Vice President, John and Mary R. Markle Foundation

DAVID D. RUTSTEIN
>Head, Department of Preventive Medicine, Harvard University Medical School

† DAVID SARNOFF
>Chairman of the Board, Radio Corporation of America

PARTICIPANTS

† RICHARD K. SCALES
   General Manager, Research and Engineering Department,
   Ethyl Corporation

GEORGE S. SCHAIRER
   Director of Research, Boeing Airplane Company

CHARLES H. SCHAUER
   Vice President, Research Corporation

PAUL A. SCHERER
   Executive Officer, Carnegie Institution of Washington

FRANCIS O. SCHMITT
   Institute Professor of Biology, Massachusetts Institute of
   Technology

* FRANK K. SCHOENFELD
   Vice President, Research, B. F. Goodrich Company

PAUL B. SEARS
   Chairman, Conservation Program, Yale University

† THOMAS J. SHANAHAN
   President, Federation Bank and Trust Company

* JAMES A. SHANNON
   Director, National Institutes of Health

* HARRY L. SHAPIRO
   Curator of Physical Anthropology and Chairman, Department of Physical Anthropology, American Museum of Natural History

† DALE E. SHARP
   President, Morgan Guaranty Trust Company of New York

GEORGE G. SIMPSON
   Curator of Fossil Mammals and Chairman, Department of
   Geology and Paleontology, American Museum of Natural
   History

B. FREDERICK SKINNER
   Professor of Psychology, Harvard University

HOWARD E. SKIPPER
   Assistant Director, Southern Research Institute

† ELLIS D. SLATER
   Chairman of the Board, Emery Air Freight Corporation

† ALFRED P. SLOAN, JR.
   President, Alfred P. Sloan Foundation

† Raymond P. Sloan
   Vice President, Alfred P. Sloan Foundation
Joseph E. Smadel
   Associate Director, National Institutes of Health
* Lloyd P. Smith
   Vice President, Avco Manufacturing Company
Waldo E. Smith
   Executive Secretary, American Geophysical Union
Henry D. Smyth
   Professor of Physics, Princeton University
† Major General Howard McC. Snyder
   Physician to the President
† W. Cordes Snyder, Jr.
   Chairman and President, Blaw-Knox Company
Tracy M. Sonneborn
   Distinguished Service Professor of Zoology, Indiana University
† Frank H. Sparks
   President, Council for Financial Aid to Education
* Frank H. Spedding
   Professor of Physical Chemistry and Director, Institute of Atomic Research, Iowa State College
† Herman J. Spoerer
   Vice President, Youngstown Sheet and Tube Company
† Frank J. Starzel
   General Manager, Associated Press
William C. Steere
   Director, New York Botanical Garden
I. Melville Stein
   President, Leeds and Northrup Company
* H. Burr Steinbach
   Chairman, Department of Zoology, University of Chicago
† Herman W. Steinkraus
   Chairman of the Board, Bridgeport Brass Company
† Thomas E. Stephens
   Secretary to the President
Earl P. Stevenson
   President, Arthur D. Little, Inc.

PARTICIPANTS

* William E. Stevenson
 President, Oberlin College

 H. Guyford Stever
 Professor of Aeronautical Engineering, Massachusetts Institute of Technology

† Richard M. Stewart
 President, American Brass Company

 C. Chester Stock
 Associate Director, Sloan-Kettering Institute for Cancer Research

 Sigvard E. Strandh
 Scientific Attaché, Swedish Embassy

* Julius A. Stratton
 President, Massachusetts Institute of Technology

 William L. Straus, Jr.
 Professor of Physical Anthropology, Johns Hopkins University

† T. Laurence Strimple
 President, National Acme Company

* C. Guy Suits
 Vice President and Director of Research, General Electric Company

† Leon A. Swirbul
 President, Grumman Aircraft Engineering Corporation

 Edward L. Tatum
 Member, Rockefeller Institute

† Hugh S. Taylor
 Editor, *American Scientist*

† Hon. Olin E. Teague
 Congressman from Texas

* W. Furness Thompson
 Vice President, Smith, Kline and French Laboratories

† J. T. Thurston
 Technical Director, Agricultural Division, American Cyanamid Company

* Max Tishler
 President, Merck Sharp & Dohme Research Laboratories Division

† ADOLPH TOIGO
President, Lennen and Newell, Inc.

† VIRGINIA J. TOLSON
Alfred P. Sloan Foundation

† JAMES E. TRAINER
Executive Vice President, Firestone Tire and Rubber Company

MERRIAM H. TRYTTEN
Director, Office of Scientific Personnel, National Academy of Sciences—National Research Council

† CHARLES H. TUTTLE
Breed, Abbott and Morgan

* MERLE A. TUVE
Director, Department of Terrestrial Magnetism, Carnegie Institution of Washington

† WILLIAM E. UMSTATTD
President, Timken Roller Bearing Company

CASSIUS J. VAN SLYKE
Associate Director, National Institutes of Health

ERNEST H. VOLWILER
Chairman of the Board, Abbott Laboratories

* T. F. WALKOWICZ
Associate of Laurance S. Rockefeller

† HELLMUTH WALTER
Director of Research, Worthington Corporation

* ALAN T. WATERMAN
Director, National Science Foundation

† ROBERT E. WATERMAN
Vice President, Schering Corporation

JAMES D. WATSON
Assistant Professor of Biology, Harvard University

† WILLIAM W. WATSON
Professor of Physics, Yale University

* WARREN WEAVER
Vice President for Natural and Medical Sciences, Rockefeller Foundation

† PAUL WEBBINK
Vice President, Social Science Research Council

PARTICIPANTS

† ERNST WEBER
> President, Polytechnic Institute of Brooklyn

HAROLD C. WEBER
> Chief Scientific Adviser, Department of the Army

* PAUL A. WEISS
> Head, Laboratory of Developmental Biology, Rockefeller Institute

FRITS W. WENT
> Director, Missouri Botanical Garden

† JESSE WERNER
> Vice President, General Aniline and Film Corporation

F. JOACHIM WEYL
> Research Director, Office of Naval Research

JOHN A. WHEELER
> Professor of Physics, Princeton University

FRED L. WHIPPLE
> Professor of Astronomy, Harvard University, and Director, Astrophysical Observatory of the Smithsonian Institution

* DOUGLAS M. WHITAKER
> Vice President for Administration, Rockefeller Institute

† ALEXANDER M. WHITE
> White, Weld and Company

† C. M. WHITE
> Chairman of the Board, Republic Steel Corporation

WILLIAM M. WHYBURN
> Vice President for Graduate Studies and Research and Acting Provost, University of North Carolina

* JEROME B. WIESNER
> Professor of Electrical Engineering and Director, Research Laboratory of Electronics, Massachusetts Institute of Technology

† FRAZAR B. WILDE
> President, Connecticut General Life Insurance Company

† W. BRADFORD WILEY
> President, John Wiley and Sons, Inc.

* SAMUEL S. WILKS
> Professor of Mathematical Statistics, Princeton University

307

JOHN H. WILLIAMS
>   Director, Division of Research, U. S. Atomic Energy Commission

† PERRY WILLIAMS
>   President, Kelsey-Hayes Company

ROBLEY C. WILLIAMS
>   Professor of Biophysics, University of California

HARRY WILLIAMSON
>   Scientific Attaché, Canadian Embassy

JOHN T. WILSON
>   Assistant Director for Biological and Medical Sciences, National Science Foundation

PERRY W. WILSON
>   Professor of Bacteriology, University of Wisconsin

* ROBERT E. WILSON
>   Former Chairman of the Board, Standard Oil Company (Indiana)

† WALTER W. WILSON
>   Morgan Stanley and Company

HARRY A. WINNE
>   Director, American Electric Power Company

* DAEL WOLFLE
>   Executive Officer, American Association for the Advancement of Science

* DANA YOUNG
>   Dean, School of Engineering, Yale University

DONALD YOUNG
>   President, Russell Sage Foundation

* ARNOLD J. ZURCHER
>   Executive Director, Alfred P. Sloan Foundation

Date D
Date
PRINTED IN U. S. A.